INTERNATIONAL SERIES OF MONOGRAPHS IN
HISTORY AND PHILOSOPHY OF SCIENCE

GENERAL EDITORS: M. FLORKIN, G. A. KERKUT

VOLUME 1

A BIOLOGIST REMEMBERS

Photograph: W. Ernst Böhm

A BIOLOGIST REMEMBERS

KARL von FRISCH

Translated by

LISBETH GOMBRICH

PERGAMON PRESS

OXFORD · LONDON · EDINBURGH · NEW YORK
TORONTO · SYDNEY · PARIS · BRAUNSCHWEIG

Pergamon Press Ltd., Headington Hill Hall, Oxford
4 & 5 Fitzroy Square, London W.1
Pergamon Press (Scotland) Ltd., 2 & 3 Teviot Place, Edinburgh 1
Pergamon Press Inc., 44–01 21st Street, Long Island City, New York 11101
Pergamon of Canada, Ltd., 6 Adelaide Street East, Toronto, Ontario
Pergamon Press (Aust.) Pty. Ltd., 20–22 Margaret Street, Sydney, N.S.W.
Pergamon Press S.A.R.L., 24 rue des Écoles, Paris 5ᵉ
Vieweg & Sohn GmbH, Burgplatz 1, Braunschweig

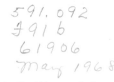

This book is a translation of *Erinnerungen eines Biologen*
originally published by Springer-Verlag, Berlin, in 1957

Library of Congress Catalog Card No. 67–16653

PRINTED IN GREAT BRITAIN BY A. WHEATON AND CO. LTD., EXETER AND LONDON
3124/67

This book is dedicated to the

AUSTRIAN ACADEMY

OF SCIENCES

CONTENTS

Foreword   ix

Where do I come from?   1

School years   18

At the university   31

Assistant at the Zoological Institute, Munich   45

Lectureship and further work as assistant in Munich   52

Interlude at the Rudolfinerhaus, 1914–1918   60

Back to zoology   68

As professor in Rostock, 1921–1923   76

Breslau, 1923–1925   90

Back in Munich   99

American journey, 1930   111

At the new institute   117

The Second World War   128

Working quietly at Brunnwinkl, 1945–1946   138

Graz, 1946–1950   146

Second journey to the States, 1949   157

To Munich for the fifth time   170

Published works   180

Index   187

FOREWORD

IT HAD never been my intention to write my autobiography. This only came about because the Austrian Academy of Sciences, of which I have been a member since 1938 and an honorary member since 1954, demands of those who belong to it that they submit for the academic record a written account of their lives of unspecified length. When, after several reminders, I sat down to this task, I found myself writing more and more, so that in fact my story will have to find a place on the Academy's book shelves rather than in their archives.

In dedicating this book to the venerable Austrian Academy of Sciences I should like this act to include my belated thanks for awarding me, with the Lieben Prize of 1921, the first scientific distinction of my career.

To Dr. Ferdinand Springer I owe a debt of gratitude for his willingness to publish my modest effort, and for the beautiful production he gave to the little book.

Brunnwinkl   KARL V. FRISCH
4 *October* 1956

WHERE DO I COME FROM?

I was born in Vienna on the 20th day of November 1886, the son of Professor Anton Ritter von Frisch and Marie, *née* Exner, his wife. My parents wanted a daughter to complete the family. Hence the late-comer—though not the wished-for little girl.

The parental home at Josefstädterstrasse 17 where I was born is still in the possession of our family. No one passing the unassuming front of the one-storey building would ever guess that behind it there lies a quiet garden, a pleasant island in a sea of houses, hardly touched by the changes inevitable when a garden suburb becomes a central residential area of a city with over a million inhabitants. From a roof terrace my father had had built towards the back, where my mother was wont to take a "breather" of an evening, her eyes would roam across neighbouring gardens to the distant outline of the Kahlenberg, and there her sense of beauty found ever new enjoyment in the glories of sunsets (Fig. 1). I remember distinctly how sad she was when the huge tenement houses began to rise all around us, cutting off our view and blocking out more and more of the sky.

My father was a surgeon who during the most glorious period of the Vienna Medical School was attached to the great Theodor Billroth as his assistant. But in order to be able to get married he resigned his post while still quite young and specialized as an urologist. In this field he achieved prominence as a practising physician, as a university teacher, and as a scientist. He also taught anatomy at the Academy of Fine Arts.

Patients flocked to his consulting rooms from Austria and beyond. During the festive seasons tokens of their gratitude, tangible and delicious, would arrive in profusion, ranging from asparagus and wine to succulent geese and suckling pigs, often decorated with the red, white, and green colours of neighbouring Hungary. His medical reputation laid the foundation of a certain modest competence

1

which secured for me and my three older brothers the enjoyment of a carefree youth and enabled us freely to choose our careers without restrictive considerations.

My mother, however, who combined gifts of mind and heart to a most unusual degree, saw to it that we never accumulated riches. She knew no greater pleasure than to give joy to others, and my

FIG. 1. My parental home, Josefstädterstrasse 17, Vienna VIII, seen from the garden. To the left the roof terrace. (*Pen and ink drawing by Jenny Frisch, née Richter, ca. 1904.*)

father, who was rather reserved and might even appear morose at times, let her do as she pleased. I remember a characteristic instance when one day shortly before Christmas he came home and handed to her with a chuckle a great many beautiful penknives of various shapes and sizes so that she would have something to give away to her many young friends. We only occasionally heard of the help she gave so freely to many who needed it for she never mentioned these things which were, to her, all in a day's work.

It must not be thought, however, that she had no imagination beyond the daily round. Quite early in their married life, when money was by no means plentiful, she persuaded her reluctant husband to buy a large, rambling but solidly built 300-year-old mill at Brunnwinkl near St. Gilgen on Lake Wolfgang. This was the

FIG. 2. My paternal grandfather, Dr. Anton Ritter von Frisch, Physician on the General Staff, Austro-Hungarian Army.

beginning of a family holding which soon grew and was to survive two world wars, offering a haven of peace where contemplation, recreation, and steady work remained possible in troubled times.

But first I want to talk about my forebears (see the pedigree at the end of the book). Our "nobility" is not of long standing. My father's father (Fig. 2) was a surgeon in the Austrian Imperial

Army. In 1877 he was honoured with the order of the Iron Cross, 3rd class, for his services in reorganizing the Army Medical Corps, and this decoration carried with it an hereditary knighthood. His father had also been a doctor, and two of his sons, as well as four of his grandsons, chose a medical career. While medicine was thus

Fig. 3. My maternal grandfather, Dr. Franz Exner, Professor of Philosophy at Prague University. (*Lithograph by Kriehuber, 1831.*)

the chief tradition on my father's side, we probably inherited the leaning towards research and scholarship from my mother's family. My grandfather, Franz Exner (Fig. 3), had been a Professor of Philosophy at the University of Prague. His lectures roused the enthusiasm of his undergraduate listeners, and an address "On the position of students at a university", given on the occasion of matriculation when he was Dean of the Faculty in 1834, is one of the most beautiful speeches I know, both as regards form and ethical content. In 1848 he was sent to Vienna to prepare new curricula at the Ministry of Education. He it was who was chiefly responsible for the plans to reform Austrian secondary and university education which were to remain models of such plans for decades.

In 1853 my grandfather, already a sick man, went to northern Italy, which at that time was still part of the Austro-Hungarian monarchy, as a commissioner for Italian schools. Soon afterwards he died an untimely death at Padova.

Franz Exner's father had been a customs officer in Vienna; his mother, the owner of a vineyard in the near-by Grinzing. As his wife he chose Charlotte Dusensy, the daughter of a banker and business man from Prague. Though she had been baptized soon after birth, she was of Jewish extraction. This has later caused us a good deal of trouble which fortunately my dear mother could not foresee while she lived. But there is no doubt that the mixture was a good one, for all five children of the marriage developed into exceptional personalities.

They lost both their parents at a tender age. A friend of the family, Frau Julie von Ladenburg, befriended Marie, my mother; she took her into her home in Vienna until such time that her brothers would be old enough to look after her (Fig. 4). It is remarkable that, despite adverse circumstances, all four boys not only went to university but so distinguished themselves academically that each one of them ended up as a professor. Adolf, the eldest, became a Professor of Roman Law at Zürich. Karl started as a master in a secondary school but later occupied a chair of mathematics at Innsbruck University. Sigmund became Professor of Physiology and Director of the Institute of Physiology at Vienna University, and Franz Serafin Professor of Physics and Director of the Institute of Physics, also in Vienna.

Thrown upon their own resources at an early age, the four brothers and their sister developed an exceptionally close and intimate relationship. My mother (Fig. 5), who was exactly in the middle of the family by age, took the keenest interest in everything that concerned her menfolk, not only in their tribulations and triumphs but also in their intellectual pursuits. Having grown up

FIG. 4.   My mother's four brothers with their "Aunt Toni", an
unmarried sister of their deceased father. *From left to right:* Adolf,
Franz Serafin, Sigmund, and Karl Exner. (*After a coloured
photograph.*)

in such a lively intellectual climate she completely lacked interest in idle female gossip. She liked to sit quietly in a corner, listening to the stimulating talk of bright and eager young men around her and occasionally joining in their conversation with some shrewd and penetrating questions.

Adolf was the first to reach the consummation of an academic career. He was called to the Chair of Roman Law at Zürich, and his sister joined him there. It was during that time that a close and

FIG. 5. My mother, Marie Exner, 1871.

intimate friendship developed between the Exners and Gottfried Keller, the great Swiss poet. This has become quite well known through a correspondence which continued, off and on, to the end of the poet's life. True, they did not meet very often in Zürich, because soon after their first encounter Adolf was called to a Chair in Vienna. But in the summer of 1873 Keller accepted an invitation from brother and sister to visit them at See am Mondsee in the Salzkammergut (the Austrian Lake District) where they and some of their friends were spending a summer holiday.

A few passages from letters that passed between Zürich and Vienna following this visit will give some idea of the mood of relaxed good humour with which this famous elderly eccentric, well known for his grouchiness and lack of sociability, responded to the harmless gaiety of his Austrian friends, and show how unerringly Marie Exner found the right light-hearted tone that made this response possible. The letters deal among other things with an exchange of small Christmas gifts between Gottfried Keller and the Exner household.

Zürich, 19 October 1873

Most gracious young lady,

Feeling slightly bored, it occurs to me that nothing in the world could stop me, silly fellow though I am, from procuring for myself some pleasant diversion by penning a letter to my amusing friends abroad. But since the Professor is not in the habit of replying, I name you head of the firm and address my screed to you.

First, I have to report that I arrived safely in my native land— but that was a whole eternity ago.

But I really meant to thank you all once more for being so kind to me and treating me so well, and this I am doing herewith. Before Xmas I will send you my grandmother's earrings in case you want to dress up again in 18th century costume during the next carnival season. You need not hesitate to accept them. They are not worth much.

Yesterday I went with an Old Boys' Club to the Falls of the Rhine on an autumn outing where we drank new wine and old champagne. I made some atrocious speeches; now I am full of remorse, and heavy of head and heart; and all of a sudden I think of poor little Sophie at Mondsee, her tears and her cakes. Oh dear! What are you doing? Are you busy painting lovely pictures? Are you well and cheerful? Perhaps, in a few weeks, you might consider writing me, say, a half page of your news. . . .

Yours devotedly,
G. KELLER

Vienna, 5 November 1873

Dear Mr. Keller,

Please forgive me, if you can, for not waiting the requisite number of weeks before I send you my reply. Your letter gave me too much pleasure for me to be able to keep quiet for any length of time. I am not normally a good correspondent, nor am I really very talkative, but with you I turn into a proper chatterbox—I suppose because you yourself don't talk much as a rule, and yet one would so much like to make you, for listening to you is such a joy. So please don't be cross with me if I keep prodding you and worrying you. During our holiday at Mondsee I often had the feeling that I tired you with my fidgeting, but I just could not help myself. It was too strong for me. If one is full to bursting point of devotion, admiration, joy and gratitude and cannot contain oneself, one is apt to behave rather like that. . . .

Our life is generally very peaceful, but on alternate Sundays the men go shooting hares. Then there is the devil to pay! The whole day long they go without a hot meal and in the evening when the whole gang invades the house, they are simply ravenous. It is very much like in holiday time. . . . Everybody sends his love and everybody expects you to visit us in spring. You will have a room with a separate entrance, where you will be completely undisturbed by man or beast, and I will be so quiet that you will hardly notice I am there. I don't know how to thank you for your charming idea to send me your grandmother's earrings. But I really have scruples about accepting them. You told me once that they always lie on your inkstand and that you are in the habit of playing with them when you collect your thoughts. What if you were to miss them? Who knows how many good ideas are contained in the trinkets—aren't you superstitious at all? But joking apart, I accept the thought for the deed and thank you a thousand times for your intention! ! !

Adolf sends his love, he will write you soon. God bless you! Shall we hear from you again?

Yours,
MARIE EXNER

Zürich, 20 December 1873

From the way you try to protect yourself from receiving those earrings, my very dear Miss Marie Exner, one would think that they had once belonged to the grandmother of a certain other gentleman, and not to mine! But you cannot escape my little avuncular attentions quite so easily. For I have hit immediately on another scheme: I have made a picture of one of those mountain paths you made me walk, or rather wade and wobble through, and I am sending you this product as a small Christmas present, with my best wishes for the New Year. But so that I should always be in a position to deny the authorship of this daub (it is 12 years since I last dabbled in water colours) I have attributed it to you; if you take a magnifying glass, you will be able to see the inscription in the top right-hand corner. A second little picture, showing the forest path to Unterach, with the Höllengebirge range in the background, is unfortunately not quite finished yet, I shall be sending it later.

I wonder myself whether I shall get to Vienna next year? We shall have to wait and see whether life and health will allow it. But if I really do come to do some work in the little garden room you have assigned to me, you will have to pull yourselves together and lead a sober, sensible, life. All this punch-drinking will have to stop and a puritanical austerity will have to take its place. To this end I shall have to equip myself with a wardrobe made of American cloth or possibly rubber—so that the punch and wine stains won't be so conspicuous. . . .

Have a jolly time in the festive season, my dear, and don't feed your huntsmen too well. Do they ever manage to bring any game home at all?

Yours very sincerely,
G. KELLER

Vienna, 27 December 1873

My dearest, kindest, and most excellent Mr. Keller,

Please don't be angry with me for my excessive admiration, I shall rid myself of this habit, you will see, just bear with me a little longer! First, I must tell you that I find your little picture of Lake Mondsee so charming, so beautiful, so full of sunshine and delight that my heart leaps within me every time I look at it. I thank you a thousand times for the whole consignment. . . . As regards the earrings, I must confess that if you had seen the expression of mixed feelings on my face when I put my protestations against this gift down on paper, you would probably have had pity on me and sent them to me after all. But at the moment I am terribly pleased with the picture which otherwise I should never have received! However, I would like to make a suggestion. Remove the earrings from your desk for a while to see what happens. If it turns out that this has no harmful effect on your writing, you may send them to me, after a year and a day have gone by.

We are busy weeding and planting in front of your future window, and we shall expect your arrival as soon as the first buds burst open in spring. We will provide you with suitable rough clothing. The huntsmen partly send their greetings, partly greet you themselves. They do indeed bring many hares home, but they eat more than they provide. A happy New Year!

Yours,
MARIE E.

Zürich, 3 January 1874

My sweetest and dearest Miss Exner and Co.,

The box with the presents—partly Christian-Teutonic, partly classical in nature—arrived here safely. I am completely overwhelmed. Such extravagance! . . .

The tree arrived in good condition: only some of the little bottles were empty, their wee bellies crushed. I said to them: "This is no way to turn up, you fools. How can I now obtain anything from you, you faithless messengers?" But they did not even say they were sorry! Most of them had, however, arrived intact, thanks to your touching efforts in packing them so carefully with your own sweet hands. As to the books, I imagine that you begged them from your three brothers like the dear little princess in the fairy tale, who when she met a poor old charcoal burner in the woods, ran home and asked her three brothers for their supper to give to the old man. Three of them let her have it, but the fourth was away, shooting the innumerable birds of prey that darkened the sky at the time. And with what kindness, forbearance and tact you free me from my spleen about those earrings! However, it will not take the whole of a twelvemonth, for I have already put them away some time ago. I therefore send them to you straight away. . . .

You cannot imagine how grateful I am. My gratitute will soon become so habitual that it may even bring about some sort of permanent change in my humour! You try to beat that!

GOTTFRIED KELLER

Vienna, 10 January 1874

My very dear, but nevertheless very naughty, Mr. Keller!

The way you treat your own generous and deepfelt words of thanks as part of a game, and likewise my own effusions, is really devilish, and if I had not had to laugh so heartily at the clever way in which you choke off my thanks, I should have been furious. But from now on you are safe. Henceforth I shall never say "thank-you" for anything any more, but should I suddenly die without a trace of bodily ill, *you* will know the cause. . . .

Keller's planned visit to Vienna took place in the summer of 1874. In that special garden room at Josefstädterstrasse 17, where he stayed with the Exners, he worked on his long short story *Das verlorene Lachen* (The Lost Laughter).

My parents were married on 19 November, 1874. No doubt their happy circle of friends provided lots of fun and merry wit on the occasion, especially at the stag party on the eve of the wedding, but the only memento extant is a telegram Gottfried Keller sent from Zürich:

Fresh the weather be and fine,
Witches wed today,
Merry feasting, meat and wine,
Friends in gay array.*

Macht frisch Wetter heut',
Hexen tun heiraten,
Um den Tisch sind schöne Leut',
Lustig dampft der Braten.

By my hearth I sit with glee,
Smoke, think of your laughter,
Wishing you that you may be
Happy ever after.

Hinter'm Ofen sitz' ich froh,
Brauch mich nicht zu zieren,
Rauch' mein Pfeiflein Haberstroh
Und tu' gratulieren.

Joyful music fills the air,
Sounds of hope and mirth.
Broomstick, you stay in your lair
Heaven's come to earth.

In den Lüften klingt und weht
Überall ein Hoffen,
Besen in der Ecke steht
Und der Himmel offen.

Fɪɢ. 6.   My mother, Marie von Frisch, soon after her marriage,
1875.

---

* The first stanza in the original is a pun on the names of bride and
bridegroom—*frisch* being German for fresh, and the German for witch,
Hexe, is very similar to Exner.

My parents spent several holidays in the lovely Salzkammergut region and knew it well. At that time the district was not on the railway, rarely visited by holiday makers, and not yet disfigured by the rash of ugly buildings which inevitably follows the influx of tourists. In the summer of 1882 they rented rooms in the water mill at Brunnwinkl on Lake Wolfgang which has

FIG. 7. The mill-house at Brunnwinkl (built 1615/16). In the background, the Schafberg. (*Oil painting by Marie von Frisch,* ca. *1884.*)

already been mentioned. My three brothers were 7, 5 and 4 years old at the time and I myself had not yet put in an appearance. Despite the fact that the region is notorious for its wet climate, and undeterred by the weather which during that summer had been even worse than usual, my mother (Fig. 6) fell in love with the idyllic spot and recognized its potentialities. When the owner of the mill, who happened to be deeply in debt, begged them to buy the property, my parents made up their minds on the spot to purchase the mill-house (Fig. 7) and some of the land that went with it. We have a letter my mother wrote to Gottfried Keller about the transaction.

22 December, 1882

My dear Mr. Keller,

. . . True, it has again rained buckets in our limestone fastness, but the rain notwithstanding we were so happy there that we decided, frivolously, to buy the old mill where we have been staying when that ramshackle old building that once had been a comfortable farm house, and a good bit of land besides, was offered to us for 3000 florins—no money to speak of for spendthrift Viennese like us.

One of my most fervent wishes has thus come true: I shall be able to spend all future summers and Indian summers of my life on the same beloved spot. My husband, too, finds a lot of pleasure there. Fishing, nine-pin bowling (we have a bowling alley of our own), shooting (roe deer and red deer, chamois, not ravens or lizards), sailing, swimming, etc. So if we live, it will be most enjoyable, and you are most cordially invited to the usual house-warming. I hope that by autumn I shall have built, nailed, painted, and cleaned in and about the house to such an extent that an indulgent visitor may stay there in moderate comfort. . . .

To which Gottfried Keller replied:

Zürich, 29 December 1882

Dear Mrs. von Frisch,

. . . So you have bought an old mill near a mountain lake. No doubt there will also be a mill stream, and all the necessary paraphernalia, so that we may hope for a new cycle of millers' songs* from Lake Wolfgang. I want you to grind nothing but lovely, cheerful white flour through all the summers of your life, until your dark hair becomes dusted with it. You will then need no powder to hide the fact; but may this be a long way off!

After the old flourmill had ceased functioning it was turned into a commodious summer residence of nine rooms without much change in its outward appearance. The former owners used the purchase money to build a smaller dwelling house as an annexe to their sawmill (which was still working) some 100 yards away, but 4 years later the sawmill, too, was laid still (Fig. 8).

---

* The allusion is, of course, to Schubert's song cycle.

Fig. 8. Brunnwinkl. In the foreground the sawmill with annexe. Behind it is the gable of the old mill-house, to the right of the large boat house the "Schusterhaus", half hidden by trees; to the left in front of the knoll the roof of the "Fischerhaus". The "Jockelhaus", to the far left, is no longer in the picture. (*Photograph taken in 1885.*)

Fig. 9. Brunnwinkl today. In the centre the mill-house, to the left thereof, partly hidden by trees, the converted sawmill. On the far left the "Fischerhaus", to the right the "Schusterhaus". (*Photograph F. Baader, 1956.*)

My father bought it and converted it, together with the dwelling house attached, into two summer villas. The miller and his people moved away, but our families continued to keep in touch for a long time.

In the years that followed my father used his savings chiefly to add to his Brunnwinkl property. He bought not only pastures and woodlands, but also two more houses (the "Schuster" in 1888, the "Jockl" in 1902). Only one of the local dwellings remained in the possession of a small farmer whose family lives there still. These six houses, scattered on either side of the mill stream over some low-lying meadowland bounded by the lake on one side and woody slopes on the remaining sides, comprise the hamlet of Brunnwinkl.

At that time there was only one road, the road from Lake Mondsee. It came down one of the nearby slopes and we could often hear the merry tune of the post horn when the mail coach descended the steep gradient to our lake. When later, in 1893, the Salzkammergut narrow-gauge railway was built along that same slope, it brought many visitors and many changes. But since I do not intend to write a history of Brunnwinkl all this is really by the way.

What is, however, relevant to our story is the way the houses of the little colony were occupied. The Old Mill, the centre of it all, was the permanent summer residence of my parents and us boys. The other houses, all furnished for summer occupation in the same rustic style, were let to three of my mother's brothers and their families, rents being asked (and paid) more as a matter of form than for the sake of profit. Only Adolf, the eldest, had his own summer place in the Tyrol. The fifth house was usually let to friends (not necessarily the same people each year), thus providing a welcome element of change in the small colony. Not that this was the only source of variety; all the houses were big enough to receive guests, and usually there were plenty of people staying. My mother would dearly have liked Gottfried Keller to come and see her little domain. In her last letter to him, dated 9 April, 1890, she wrote: ". . . Next summer we shall all go to our dear Lake Wolfgang again and it would fulfil one of my most cherished dreams to have you there with us, to entertain you, look after you and generally cosset you to my heart's content. . . ."

It was to remain a dream. Gottfried Keller died in July of that year.

One of the unwritten laws of the Brunnwinkl community was that people were left alone to do as they pleased, guests included. You could live like a hermit for days if you wanted to, though generally there was much completely spontaneous and informal visiting between the houses in the evenings, small parties meeting one night in one, in another the next. Though the young people would often keep to themselves, laughing and playing and teasing each other with innocent banter, on some nights they would be equally prepared to listen to serious talk when one of their elders told about travels to foreign lands or when recent advances of science were being discussed. The scope for such discussions was widened by the many friends who used to come for short or long visits. Theodor Billroth, who had taken a liking to these parts soon after my parents had settled there, built for himself a summer residence no more than a few hundred yards away; many of the visitors that thronged his hospitable musical house (where Brahms was frequently an honoured guest) would drop in at Brunnwinkl. The great Austrian writer Marie von Ebner-Eschenbach, who spent several summers at the neighbouring resort of St. Gilgen, read quite a few of her works from manuscript to our small circle. The life we led was thus both stimulating and healthy, for, without any special stress being laid on sport, it was natural in these surroundings that we all became good swimmers and climbers, and ardent nature lovers. Presiding over it all was my mother, the uncrowned queen of this pleasant domain, whose graceful poise and conciliatory charm welded our little community into a harmonious whole.

SCHOOL YEARS

To BEGIN with I was educated privately at home. For the last year of junior school I was sent to the convent school of the Piarist Fathers close to where we lived. By the time I started in the lowest form of the "Humanist Gymnasium" (secondary school on classical lines) my brother Ernst was in the eighth and last form, and my

FIG. 10.   Early beginnings. Karl Frisch, *ca.* 1889.

two older brothers were already at the university, studying, respectively, law and medicine. This meant that I grew up almost like an only child, and I might have been expected to feel attracted by friends of my own age group. Actually, I had little inclination that way. I was much more drawn to playmates from the world of animals.

Every year in the autumn my mother would buy a blue tit from a pet shop and tend it all through the winter, allowing it to fly

18

about in our sitting room for hours on end. When spring came, the bird was set free. I remember that the care and tenderness lavished on our little room-mate made a deep impression on my mind, and that her indignation at any act of cruelty to animals made me aware of animals as conscious beings at an early stage.

Even before I went to school I had a little zoo in my room. At that time we used to spend a few days every Whitsuntide at the Hungarian estate of some friends of ours. There the countryside abounded in ponds peopled with frogs and newts. To catch them, take them with me to Vienna, and there to tend and observe them, became a real passion with me. I could sit in front of their tank for hours watching their every movement. But I did not confine myself to frogs and newts for long. A rather scrappy diary from my secondary school days, which has been preserved, lists among the animals which I had been tending at that time 9 different species of mammals, 16 species of birds, 26 of cold-blooded terrestrial vertebrates, 27 of fish, and 45 species of non-vertebrates. I shall always be grateful to my mother for her indulgence towards these house guests which cannot, after all, have been invariably pleasant. I must also thank my father (Fig. 11) for his infrequent but well-timed suggestions. I remember how one day he called me into his surgery after the last patient had gone and, making me look through the miscroscope (normally used to study urine sediments), introduced me to the world of the microscopic organisms. He had actually grown cultures especially for the purpose of showing them to me. Another time he travelled with me right across Vienna to see a man whose hobby was aquaria—heaven knows how he had heard about him—to be shown his equipment and his breeds of exotic fish. This man taught me how to make a proper aquarium, and I followed his instructions with good results. I had many fresh- and sea-water aquaria which were a source of great pleasure to me and incidentally provided, effortlessly, some excellent training in observation.

After a serious illness, my mother went south for a few weeks as soon as spring came. She took me with her to the quiet little village of Lovrana on the east coast of Istria, not far from the better-known resort of Abbazzia (Opatia). The creatures I found on the shores of the Adriatic were incomparably more colourful than those I had encountered on the banks of Lake Wolfgang, and I had the most exciting surprises. I loved to lie for hours between the cliffs, motionless, watching the living things I could see on and between the slimy green stones just below the surface of the water. I discovered that miraculous worlds may reveal themselves to a patient observer where the casual passer-by sees nothing at all. It

FIG. 11.   My father, Professor Dr. Anton Ritter von Frisch.

goes without saying that after each such visit to the Adriatic coast my sea-water aquarium received some fresh inmates. Some of them I managed to keep for years.

Two of my animal friends I want to mention specially:

I cannot have been more than 6 or 7 years old when I woke one morning from a knocking at the garden window. When I opened it, a speckled woodpecker flew straight into the room. We soon found out that he had escaped from some boys who had taken him out of his nest and reared him by hand. When he found himself starving he had asked to be let in at our house. The bird was bought straight away from his rightful owners and in no time had established the whole room as his cage. He was very cunning and managed to escape from us, too, but we had only to show him the earthenware pot which he had come to know as an inexhaustible source of mealworms, his favourite food, to entice him back. When we took Ignaz with us to Brunnwinkl there were so many opportunities to escape from the room when the weather was fine that he soon acquired the habit of spending the day in the surrounding woodlands but he always returned at night—whether for the sake of the mealworms, or because he was attached to us, who can tell? On days when we took our midday meal out of doors, Ignaz was sure to turn up as soon as soup was served and, after a drum solo played on the rain pipe, to demand his flesh pot. Once, when my mother went for a walk in the nearby forest with some friends who had just dropped in, she noticed our Ignaz among the fir trees and called him, whereupon he alighted on the top of her head and greeted her by drumming with his beak. Naturally her friends were most impressed to see her so intimate with the birds of the forest. One day he failed to return. We never learned whether he had felt the call of his own kin, or whether he had had an accident.

With a small parrot given to me by some friends when I was about 8 years old I developed a much closer and more lasting friendship. The bird was a Brazilian parakeet with bright green plumage, somewhat larger than the more common budgerigars. He became very attached to me and I to him. During the years I went to school, and even later when I studied at Vienna University, he used to be my constant companion at home, sitting upon my shoulder, dozing in my lap, nibbling at the papers and pencils on my desk, or otherwise engaged about my person. He was never absent at meal times, and, gourmet that he was, always knew exactly where to find the choicest morsels. I myself could do what I liked with him, but he kept himself aloof from other members of the family and even more so from strangers. He showed his character by pecking my brother's finger even when he offered him something especially nice because Hans did occasionally like to tease him a bit. At night he slept next to my bed, and first thing every morning

I would reach into his cage to pick him up and talk to him. This sort of intimate relationship presupposed a minimum of habit training. As he was only allowed out when he had produced "a spot" in his cage, he soon learned to produce minute quantities without inner compulsion for the sake of this reward, and his frantic efforts in this respect were sometimes very funny to watch. And because I would lock him in his cage when he had misbehaved he usually showed signs of unrest when he felt an urge, though he never actually learned to go back to his cage by himself. In fact, he never quite understood the situation. That he was allowed out after producing a dropping appears to have made a bigger impression on his little brain than the opposite sequence of events, so that somehow the act of pressing as such became, in his imagination, associated with reward, and even when he was outside his cage, he would sometimes "beg" in this peculiar manner—for instance if he saw a titbit he fancied or something else he liked. He lived with us for some 15 years. I was a student at Munich University when my mother told me in a letter the sad news that Tschocki had died in her hands after a short illness.

There was nothing deliberate or intentional in this intensive occupation with animals. I simply enjoyed watching the manifestations of their biological functions and mental stirrings in all the variety related to the different stages of animal development. Even then I wanted to record what I saw and communicate it to others, possibly under the influence of the many nature books I used to read so avidly. While still at school I occasionally sent notes on some minor observation to journals for amateur naturalists which actually were published. One such observation, published in the *Blätter für Aquarien- und Terrarienkunde,* concerned the light sensitivity of sea anemones. I had noticed that these creatures of my sea-water aquarium began to wave their tentacles when I put the light on. This struck me as peculiar, since they have no eyes, and I made some experiments to test the extent of their reaction and to find out whether they really responded to light or rather to a rise in temperature. One evening at supper I handed the article which had just appeared and of which I was, admittedly, rather proud to my uncle, the physiologist Sigmund Exner. He gave it his serious attention and made some appreciative remark about it. This surprised my aunt who, sitting next to him, had looked over his shoulder; she asked why he was so pleased with a piece of writing that to her seemed dry and uninspired. He replied: "The communication contains all that is relevant and nothing that is redundant. Wrapping the facts in elegant verbiage is something he will no doubt learn soon enough!" This was the first time those leisure activities which were to become my life's work received encouragement and recognition from someone competent to judge, and that is why the incident has stayed in my memory.

I remember far more about my animals than about school. And though I do recall that I had to take my entrance examination for the *Schottengymnasium** alone in the director's room some days before the rest of the boys because we were about to leave for Brunnwinkl, I could not now name a single question on any paper. Yet I remember vividly how my attention was so distracted by some flies crawling on the window pane that the director tried, without success, to catch them or chase them away.

Apart from animals I was greatly interested in the achievements of technology, like other boys. Admittedly aeroplanes were not yet able to kindle the imagination of youngsters, for they were not yet out of the nursery themselves. I can still remember a demonstration flight announced by a French pioneer of aviation. Crowds of Viennese had flocked to the flood plain of the Danube one Sunday morning to see if the aeroplane would fly. It tried repeatedly, but only taxied along the ground until on one such run it accidentally hit a stone, whereupon it jumped into the air and continued for some 100 to 200 yards just above ground level. Thunderous applause rewarded this achievement.

My boyish enthusiasm was naturally much more concerned with railways and boats. Through many a summer the bowling alley at Brunnwinkl was for me a railway train in which I travelled all over the world, sometimes as driver, at other times as guard. In town, the roads through which I went to school became in my imagination mighty rivers and canals on which I navigated my small fictitious motor-boats from one bank to the other. These were, of

---

* A classical school of the highest reputation, run by members of a Benedictine convent founded during the Middle Ages by monks from Scotland.

C

course, ages ahead of their time in technical perfection! However, I must confess that I accepted the miracles of technology without much thinking, and never felt inclined to go to a lot of trouble to understand them.

I was never good at school and definitely had no gift for either languages or mathematics. From the first to the last form I had to have special coaching in Latin and Greek from an outstanding classical scholar, one Dr. Löhr, whom I must have pained a good deal through my persistent ignorance of Latin verbs and my imperviousness to the rules of grammar.

Some of the Benedictine monks who taught at the Schottengymnasium were excellent teachers. For instance, old Pater Stephen Fellner who took natural history in the higher forms. It can only have been the fault of the curriculum that even his lessons in zoology made no permanent impression on me. The teaching of physics and mathematics by Pater Benedikt was also of a very high order. Knowing my biological inclination and bent, he always managed to let me just slip through, though mathematics was something I just *could* not do. And because he thought that this weakness should not stand in the way of my chosen career, he helped me so efficiently in the privacy of his rooms that even in that dreaded subject all went well at the final matriculation examination.

In most subjects I had trouble with the facts, difficulties that could be overcome by dint of hard work and some coaching. But in our religious teaching I was faced with spiritual difficulties that caused me much anguish at the time. The stark doctrine that there was no salvation outside the Roman Catholic Church was directly opposed to the more liberal views held by my parents of which I soon became aware. I found it difficult to believe that the majority of the peoples on this earth should be in mortal error and that ours was the only true creed. And yet, the Good God of my lessons at school was undoubtedly the same kind Father in heaven I knew so well and trusted so implicitly since my childhood days that my thoughts would involuntarily turn to Him in serious matters even when, in later years, I was tortured by doubts as to His existence. Slowly and gradually, more under the influence of conversations I heard at home than of any religious teaching I received at school, I began to realize what a minute speck of dust our planet represents among the stellar bodies we know, and how fleeting is the existence of mankind within the history of the universe. Such convictions lead to a feeling of reverence before the Unknown, and anyone who can cast such feelings into a mould which will serve him as a support for life should be on the right road. All honest convictions deserve respect—except the presumptuous assertion that there is nothing higher in the world than the mind of man.

In my last years at school I was not interested in living animals only. I developed another passion which was to be of equal importance for my eventual career, though at that time it kept me from revising my inadequate knowledge of school subjects during the summer holidays: I started collecting, and founded the Brunnwinkl "museum". The collecting of butterflies, moths, or beetles was then, as now, a common enough pursuit of young people. It is an excellent hobby, for not only does it satisfy the passion for collecting things which most children possess, and the equally widespread delight in a chase, it also sharpens the powers of observation and presents opportunities for practising manual skills in the mounting of delicate objects. I myself did not actively succumb to this urge until I was 17 years old, but since then I have obeyed it all my life. I wanted to collect everything, not only, say, butterflies or any other selected group as most people do. On the other hand, it was obviously necessary to limit one's activities in some way, if only regionally, if the whole thing was not to get completely out of hand. Thus the plan of a local collection was formed from which all animals or other objects that did not originate in or around the Schafberg and Lake Wolfgang were to be rigorously excluded.

My new hobby was infectious. All the inhabitants of Brunnwinkl were anxious to help increase the collection, but few possessed a suitable catcher or the knowledge to handle animals. So I was continually called this way and that by the exclamation "Karl, a bug!" After a couple of years we had collected the more abundant species and I frequently had to disappoint some willing helper who wanted to show me a "rare animal" with the stereotyped remark: "Got that already." In contrast with the normal habits of collectors I did not find it in me to kill more than one representative of any species for inclusion in my collection. Not until many years later did I realize that by so doing much that is valuable is actually missed. Naturally, I made many mistakes and had to learn the hard way. After the first winter, my whole collection of insects had gone mouldy and was ruined. Three times I moved my treasures into another room. The losses only came to an end when the collection was finally installed, in 1925, in the attic storey of the old Mill House, the driest spot of our excessively damp little corner.

My collection of fish was the first section to near completion (more or less). I gave a talk on it to the people of Brunnwinkl— my very first lecture. When I had finished, my uncle Serafin (the physicist Franz Ser. Exner) mumbled something into his beard about "a newly discovered talent", a remark that gave me some (sorely needed) encouragement.

Today the zoological collection comprises *ca.* 5000 items. One of my aunts added a beautiful herbarium. My father, always anxious to further my scientific education, wanted me to include fossils, for the region is rich in ammonites and other petrefacts. A local government clerk of the neighbouring village of St. Gilgen had collected an impressive lot, and was anxious to sell us his collection as a starting point. In order to interest us in the deal—he seems to have needed money rather badly—he asked me to accompany him on a collecting trip. He stopped at a sandy slope with loam inclusions and, after a short search, extracted from it some magnificent snail shells and other less easily defined petrified objects. I was fascinated, and my father at once bought the collection. Now though I did find some additional pieces later, I never found anything nearly as good. And when I looked at these original finds at some later date with a more experienced eye, I became suspicious. Taking a hammer, I smashed one precious rarity after the other. They fell to pieces and revealed small lumps of lead with which the rascal had grouted the shells of modern marine snails so as to give them the weight of fossils. He had somehow contrived to give their exterior the right "patina", buried them in the sand, and re-unearthed them before my astonished eyes. Visitors to my museum generally take a particular interest in these fakes with their unmasked lead interiors—just as the fossils which had been cleverly faked by some mischievous persons and which Dr. J. B. H. Beringer in A.D. 1726 had *bona fide* described and reproduced in his *Lithographia Wirceburgensis* as interesting discoveries have become far more famous than the genuine fossils found by him.

While the collections were vigorously growing, I was worried by the thought of what their fate would be if I should no longer be there to look after them—for without constant care such objects soon perish. Later I realized that the value of this modest local collection lies not so much in its actual existence as in the lessons it taught me when I was building it up. I owe to it a certain knowledge of forms and a familiarity with animals of all sorts which often has been of considerable use to me.

The "museum" was also my laboratory, where most of my time that was not devoted to open-air pursuits was spent in mounting and identifying specimens: most, but by no means all. There was room for other interests in these carefree summer months. Apart from the evening gatherings already mentioned, music formed the chief counterpoise against an all too one-sided occupation with "beasties". I cannot think of the sound of stringed instruments without conjuring up the memory of my three brothers. We were born to form a string quartet (Fig. 12). Hans, the eldest, became a Professor of Constitutional Law, first at Basle University, then at Cernovice, and later, when this town was lost to Austria after the First World War, in Vienna. His chief summer pleasure was sailing. He was devoted to this sport in which he progressed from ordinary rowing boats with primitive sails to the racing yachts of the Union Yacht Club. He played the 'cello. As he was fond of handicrafts and in summer spent a good deal of his time carpentering and messing about with tools, his roughened hands not infrequently came into conflict with the ethereal sounds demanded by the music we played together.

Otto, the second, became a surgeon. He was at first assistant to Professor Eiselsberg, and later Assistant Professor of Surgery and Director of the "Rudolfinerhaus" clinic in Vienna. As such he was to become closest to me of the three through the events of later life. He was the most musical of us brothers, and played both violin and viola.

Ernst, the third, was the most modest and retired. He became Director of the Salzburg Studienbibliothek (Library of Studies) from the archives of which he unearthed the most fabulous treasures. In addition he was interested in the history of Brunn-winkl, and described its changing fortunes in charming little publications. He, too, played both the fiddle and the viola, though not so well as Otto.

I myself was the third fiddler in the family.

Fig. 12.   Our string quartet. *From left to right:* Otto, Ernst, Hans, Karl (1898).

In an unguarded moment our teacher, Julius Winkler, once remarked that you could make progress even when not practising. He meant of course that one often approaches a piece of music with better understanding and renewed zest after leaving it alone for a while. The result of my persistent attempts at achieving progress exclusively by this method was, not surprisingly, that I never got particularly far with my technique. Nevertheless, we brothers could always sit down to play a string quartet if we felt like it, and we did so frequently. My brother Otto played first violin except when our teacher and master Julius Winkler took over the first fiddle. Then we experienced our most enjoyable moments of music making. Never since have I heard Haydn's quartets played with such simplicity, beauty, and perfection. Winkler had had his own quartet at one time, and some years earlier had surprised the Vienna public with the tremendous riches of these compositions which then were largely unknown, for only a few were in the general repertoire. In later life I always made a point of visiting my old master whenever I came to Vienna. I vividly remember how enthusiastically he once talked to me about the exceptional gifts of a young pupil of his. This pupil—he was to be his last—was Wolfgang Schneiderhan.

When I was young it was customary in our circles, as it had been in those of our fathers, to reward the successful passing of the matriculation examination with an opportunity for travel. This modest equivalent of the grand tour symbolized the transition from the constraint of the schoolroom to the freedom of the world we were about to enter. All *I* wanted, however, was to get to my beloved Brunnwinkl and to my museum the moment the examination was safely behind me, there to enjoy my new freedom and the prospect of a limitless autumn. The customary journey was therefore postponed to Easter 1906. It took me to Rome.

I chose this city not only because it was the traditional goal of travellers, but also because two of my cousins happened to be staying there at the time: Nora, a daughter of my uncle Adolf Exner, and Hilde, a daughter of my uncle Franz Serafin. They were both keen painters who had gone to the Mecca of the arts for a year's serious study. They had taken lodgings in an idyllic little house in the Via Nomentana, on the outskirts of the city, and had asked me to stay with them. Both were to die young—but at that time they were healthy young women full of the joy of life, bursting with energy and enthusiasm for their art. They advised me on what to see on my visits to the city and when I returned we would spend pleasant evenings over delicious home-cooked Italian food. As far as I recollect I had only one opportunity to parade my zoological expertise: I identified the bedbugs which were brought into the house with the laundry.

During that Easter there occurred a tremendous eruption of Mt. Vesuvius, and we decided at once to travel south. When we approached Naples it became completely dark although it was midday. The train passed through a rain of ashes which penetrated through closed windows and was so fine that even the photographic plates in my camera were coated with dust. When we arrived at Naples the sky had cleared, but we waded ankle-deep in ashes.

We received unforgettable impressions from these violent and mysterious forces of nature. A stream of molten lava had passed over the little town of Boscotrecase, destroying many houses. The surface on which we stood had hardened and cooled, but through its cracks we could still see the red-hot glow underneath.

But here I anticipate. All this really belonged to my university days which will be the subject of the next chapter.

AT THE UNIVERSITY

"You don't know how lucky you are that you know what you want to be" a friend of the family once said to me, watching me build up a zoo or something of the kind on the dining room table—I must have been about 12 years old. I was very surprised, for in fact I had never given it a thought. In my last year at school the question did, however, become acute. My interest in animals was as pronounced as my lack of interest in languages, history, and so forth; and as for the law, I was convinced that only people who were not really interested in anything ever went in for that. Zoology appeared to be the obvious choice, but my father was doubtful because the material prospects of a career in zoology were not considered bright. He thought that for the sake of an assured future I should first study medicine, which would not prevent me from turning to zoology later if I still wanted to. I remember that he dangled as a bait the prospect of joining an expedition of exploration as a doctor, which he pointed out was greater than the chance of being taken on as a zoologist.

Thus it came about that in 1905 I enrolled as a student of medicine at Vienna University. On the whole I found my studies congenial, for the first 2 years of the medical course were devoted to the natural sciences and did not involve any clinical work. Only the lectures in general biology, of which I had expected most, disappointed me deeply. For what old Grobben taught was really morphology and in no way the science of life. The botanical side of biology, on the other hand, was taught admirably and with great lucidity by von Wettstein, except that the course, designed as it was for medical students, was rather elementary. Nevertheless, it led me to read with great enthusiasm the two volumes of *Pflanzenleben* (Plant Life) by Kerner von Marilaun, Wettstein's father-in-law, for this was truly biology. To physics and chemistry I applied myself conscientiously but without enthusiasm. From the

31

lectures in histology given by the venerable Professor Ebner, I remember in particular the truly beautiful and impressive microscopic slides he showed in his demonstrations. Zuckerkandl's course on human anatomy was outstanding for the clarity and vivacity of its presentation. Frequent excursions into the field of comparative anatomy formed a link with zoology. But the lectures from which I profited most for the rest of my life were the physiology lectures by my uncle Sigmund Exner. He had a reputation for being dry. His diction was slow, and he never joked. But the lucid manner in which he explained the functions of human organs, concentrating on essentials to the exclusion of everything else, was truly exemplary. Moreover, he knew how to add conviction to the spoken word by well-thought-out experiments. His lecture was the only one I heard at that time for which I took the trouble of working out my notes at home. For many years these notebooks of mine were much sought after by medical students revising for their physiology examination. The practical exercises in physiology I found equally fascinating. Watching, through the microscope, how the red corpuscles flitted through the capillaries of a frog's transparent eyelid, and later perceiving the shadows of such corpuscles on the retina of my own eye made me feel that here was indeed something that had a bearing on life itself; something that was far more exciting than the dry exercises in preparing and mounting specimens of the zoology practical.

Sigmund Exner then suggested that, as an extra, I might like to start some scientific investigation of my own at his beautiful new Physiological Institute. His own interests ranged much wider than the human physiology he taught. *Inter alia* he had published in 1891 a book on the compound eyes of crustaceans and insects which has remained, to this day, a standard work on the functioning of these marvellous organs of vision. At a time when such a discipline officially did not even exist, it represented a major work of comparative physiology in the best sense of the word. It was, therefore, quite natural for this rather unusual Professor of human physiology to suggest that I, too, should study a problem of animal physiology, but one that was very far removed from the subjects orthodox zoology was at that time interested in. He had discovered that in compound eyes there occurred certain shifts in the position of eye pigments which appeared to be connected with the alternation between daylight vision and vision in near-darkness. He wanted me to find out which position of the pigments corresponded to stimulation and which to repose. My experimental animals were lepidoptera, beetles, and shrimps.

I went to work with great enthusiasm, but very soon I was faced with a serious conflict. I had to stimulate the eyes of living crustaceans with electric currents, a manipulation which clearly was to them a most unpleasant experience. Every single experiment cost me an effort. Though finally my scientific zeal got the better of my compassion, I believe that even in later years I could not have brought myself to undertake similar research on birds or mammals with their more highly developed and presumably more sensitive nervous systems.

The eyes had also to be examined histologically. Professor Karplus who at that time was research assistant at the Institute of Physiology was my teacher in microscope technique. He was an expert. Even zoologists proper approved of my sections through the eyes of the crustaceans. But the most important lessons were those my uncle taught me himself: care in experimental work and caution in the drawing of conclusions. He was disappointed that the experiments had not provided the hoped-for answer to the question of pigment position under stimulation, probably because he thought I too would be disappointed. But I did not mind in the least. The many questions of method and some minor results completely absorbed and satisfied me. Incidentally, the reason for our failure to decide the main problem did not become clear till many years later. Then it was found that pigment shifts in crustaceans were controlled by hormones, not nerves.

After 2 years at the university (each of two terms as is customary in Germany and Austria) I passed my first medical examination with distinction in all six subjects, a fact which is here recorded in view of the results of my final examination in zoology to be mentioned later. What one is taught about the histology, anatomy, and physiology of the human body during the first 2 years of a medical course is far more detailed and thorough than anything one learns about any one animal in the course of normal zoological studies, and I have always rated this knowledge as pure gain. It provided me with a solid foundation and a permanent point of reference for all investigations into the structure and function of animal organs.

In the following year the curriculum became more medical in character and did not appeal to me any longer. The only lecture I still remember is the brilliant course on pharmacology by Hans Horst Meyer who managed to imbue this usually bone-dry subject with the spirit of physiology. My father, realizing that there was no keeping me away from zoology, consented to my changing schools in the middle of my third year. The beadle of the Faculty of Medicine was speechless. How was it possible for a young man with such excellent prospects to give up medicine! I only laughed. I should have been very surprised if someone had told me that there would come a time when I would seriously consider taking up medicine again. For then my only idea was to devote myself to zoology body and soul. But first it was necessary to decide upon a teacher. Of the two professors in Vienna, B. Hatschek was ill and K. Grobben a morphologist whose line of study did not appeal to me. The latter, when consulted, recommended Th. Boveri at Würzburg or Richard Hertwig at Munich whom he considered, rightly, the two foremost living exponents of the discipline. In the end it was decided I should go to Munich, partly no doubt because one of my cousins, Ilse Hauser (daughter of my uncle Sigmund), was married to an architect there. This meant that I, the baby of the family who hitherto had been watched over with such exceptional parental care, would not be quite alone in a strange city. Her hospitable house in Schwabing, with its lively circle of pleasant and stimulating people, was then, and always remained, a "home from home" for me.

Thus it came about that I went to Munich in the summer term of the year 1908. The Zoological Institute was housed on the second floor of the "Old Academy" in Neuhauserstrasse. Its windows gave on leafy courtyards where one would occasionally see some portly clerics from the neighbouring church of St. Michael taking a leisurely walk, or some old-age pensioners tending their roses with loving care. The building itself had once been a convent and had retained something of its former enchanted air of seclusion, though it was now filled with a lively throng of keen young undergraduates and older scientists from every country under the sun, for at that time the Zoological Institute at Munich had become the most internationally famous centre of our discipline. I do not think any other zoologist ever had as much influence on the next generation as Richard Hertwig (Fig. 13) had.

FIG. 13.   Richard von Hertwig (1927).

To a large extent this was due to his exceptional pedagogic gifts. His was the rare capacity of sifting the essential from the inessentrial, and this enabled him to explain even the most complex matters simply and lucidly both verbally and in print. When as a boy I first got hold of his book on *Actinia* which he had published in 1879 together with his brother Oscar, the future anatomist, I had, of course, no idea of zoology and had never heard the name of Hertwig. But because I knew my *Actinia* well from looking after them in my salt-water aquarium, I wanted to know what he had to say about them. It is a measure of his gift for representation that without any previous knowledge I could read, with pleasure and profit, a book designed for grown-up scientists, and gain from it a vivid conception of the structure, anatomy, and histology of these strange creatures. His textbook of zoology owed its popularity and wide distribution to this same art of lucid and impressive writing.

In personal contact, this gift was supported and enhanced by his infectious enthusiasm which communicated itself to his hearers, no matter what the subject—whether he was discussing some problem that was new to him or trying to demonstrate to a beginner some elementary facts he himself had observed thousands of times. Yet he had nothing of the schoolmaster. He was anxious that those pupils who were capable of doing so should use their own initiative, taking great interest in their ideas and never ceasing to afford them the inestimable benefit of his knowledge and experience. His kindness and the warm humanity of his personal interest in every single one of his pupils made him their trusted older friend and mentor to whom they turned not only in scientific matters but in all the vicissitudes and troubles of their lives.

However, the chief magnet that attracted old and young to Hertwig's school was his revolutionary method of research. Like most of his contemporaries he had started his career as a morphologist, but his burning desire to understand causal relationships had made him dissatisfied with mere description and had led him to question nature by means of carefully thought-out scientific experiments. He must indeed be counted among the co-founders of experimental zoology.

Of course I knew nothing of these things when I first called on Hertwig to pay my respects. His welcome was most warm and friendly and he immediately accepted me for his Lesser Zoological Practical. In my first term I profited particularly from the Professor's lectures on the Comparative Anatomy of Vertebrates, which during the summer term he usually gave on six mornings a week at the, to many, unearthly hour of 7 a.m. His style was completely lacking in rhetorical embellishments and almost dry. And yet his was the only course (apart from Exner's lectures on physiology) which impressed me sufficiently to make me work over my notes at home after each lecture. In both cases the lasting impression lay in the content and not in any brilliance of delivery.

In the following year, 1908/9, I took part in Hertwig's Major Zoological Practical. This was a thorough introduction to zoology, designed to provide a solid grounding in the anatomy and histology of all the more important phyla—something which then was by no means universal at zoological institutes. It combined in an exemplary manner the advantages of strict guidance with skilful encouragement of the student's own initiative. I received much help and valuable instruction from Richard Goldschmidt, Hertwig's chief assistant and his right-hand man. His comprehensive knowledge and lively mind did much to enliven the proceedings. Of the other lecturers, the one who interested me most was Franz Doflein, then newly appointed Assistant Professor of the Systematics and Biology of Animals (biology at that time meaning the study of the live animal). He was also in charge (under Hertwig's supervisory direction) of the Zoological Museum which was then still connected with the Zoological Institute. But he was by no means the typical museum keeper of the old school who saw his job as the hoarding of pelts and bottled specimens or the description of every new species. He never lost sight of the *living* animal and in the exhibitions destined for the public he tried with the help of a good taxidermist so to arrange his exhibits that they represented the life of the animals in beautiful groups or characteristic postures. He had collected plenty of suitable material on his expeditions to all parts of the globe. Even in Munich, minor exploring trips formed part of his every-day life, for he was a man who *had* to get out into nature. His lectures were often not so much textbook biology as colourful accounts of his exciting experiences.

He was at his best when he took us on excursions, whether these were day trips only to the Dachauer Moos, then a wild bog not yet drained for cultivation, or study tours of a few days' duration to the Dolomites. On these excursions he revealed himself as the versatile naturalist he was by inclination and natural endowment. His was a mind open to all things beautiful, and he had long been undecided whether to become a doctor, a botanist, a zoologist— or a landscape painter. He was equally good at directing his students' interest into some special limited field which they had to study in depth. To me he assigned the solitary bees, a fascinating group of insects whose nests vary between extremely primitive and highly complex structures according to species. Many a time in later years a walk planned for a day ended after a few hundred yards in front of a bees' nest from which I could not tear myself away.

Once a week the members of the Major Practical, the senior students and the assistants, assembled in the largest room of the building, a vast chamber with a vaulted roof supported by two marble columns, for Hertwig's seminar. Each of us had to report in turn on some piece of work allotted to him. Hertwig always contributed something of interest to the discussion that followed, even if—as sometimes happened for understandable reasons—he had nodded a little during the delivery of the essay itself. For my first essay I had to report on a voluminous paper by the American zoologist Jennings. It was about starfish, and dealt at length with the methods employed by these creatures to right themselves when they had fallen on their backs. These complicated acrobatics involving their many arms were difficult to describe. To enable me to demonstrate their various tricks, my landlady had very kindly made me a beautiful starfish from a piece of silk and some wadding. I carefully hid this colourful model in my breast pocket until the appropriate moment. Its sudden unexpected production caused great hilarity and this in turn gave a boost to my self-confidence. Ever since I have laid great store on vivid demonstration and the occasional surprise effect.

On Hertwig's advice I enrolled for the Easter vacation in a zoological course at Trieste, then *the* harbour of the Austro-Hungarian monarchy. Professor Cori, the head of the state-maintained Biological Institute for Marine Research, regularly held vacation courses which were chiefly frequented by undergraduates from Austria, but also attracted many students from abroad because of their high standard. The neighbouring coasts of Istria and Dalmatia are rich in scenic beauty and abound in interesting animals. Years ago, these animals had roused my untutored childish enthusiasm at Lovrana; now I was to study them in a manner befitting a zoologist, for a zoologist who has not studied the fauna of the sea at first hand is only half trained. The sea is the cradle of life. Its fauna even to this day possesses an immeasurable wealth of forms and includes organisms of the greatest primitivity and biological age, a knowledge of which is essential for the understanding of more specialized terrestrial forms. Cori not only knew the marine fauna well, he was also a stimulating teacher and himself a qualified sea captain who personally navigated the Station's trim little steamer *Adria* through the waves of its name-sake. We greatly enjoyed these pleasant and instructive interruptions of the daily routine of our course. One day he would take us to the shallow coast of Grado, where emergent land, in the shape of mud-flats, rose only slightly above the level of the sea. Another time he would trail his nets along the rocky shores near castle Duino, or he would sail to Pola harbour and the island of Brioni where monuments of bygone cultures lay buried under luxuriant subtropical vegetation. The catches we took on these excursions in deep trawl nets taught us the relationship between the nature of the sea bottom and its fauna. Sometimes things were even more exciting. We often encountered schools of dolphins, and one day it was decided that one of these creatures should die for science. The fever of the chase took hold of us all. Cori steered the boat in a bold zigzag course following that of the dolphins and finally a marksman succeeded in killing one of the animals with coarse shot. It was a female. Milk spouted from its teats when it was hauled on board. My thoughts were with the whale baby which had lost its mother.

I have always considered whaling a rather degrading undertaking. Very little is known about the life of these mammals of the high seas. But we do know that they have a highly developed brain, and nothing prevents our imagination from depicting their social and family life on a level greatly superior to that of our slow-witted cattle.*

While I was at Trieste my mother came down from Vienna for a short visit. During her stay we had a gale (the Bora) of such force that guide ropes had to be stretched along streets and across squares to prevent people from being blown out to sea. But though we could not go on the excursions we had planned, we spent

---

* *Translator's note*: Recent observations and experiments on dolphins have provided fresh evidence for this view.

many happy hours reading good books or talking about the present and the future.

I was about to return to Munich for my third term there. For it would have been the natural thing for me to continue my studies in that charming city among fellow students many of whom were my friends; and equally natural that I should ask Hertwig to suggest a subject for a thesis as soon as I had finished the Major Practical. But because my parents were very anxious to have me back with them I decided to write my thesis in Vienna.

Fortunately, experimental biology had begun to show signs of life there though the two university institutes had as yet little use for this kind of thing. On the outskirts of the town, close to Vienna's permanent fun fair, the famous *Wurstelprater* with its giant wheel, there stood the *Vivarium*. This building had once housed an aquarium and indoor zoo for the amusement of the public but had later been acquired by the zoologist Hans Przibram who had turned it into a biological research station. In his domain you did not find the pervading smell of oil of cloves and denatured spirits, for there the living animal was all important, and thither, therefore, I felt myself strongly drawn. Przibram, a man of ideas, was a gifted teacher who had gathered around him quite a number of students. In the autumn of 1909 I approached him with the request to suggest a subject for my thesis. He wanted me to work on the evolution of *Mantis religiosa*, a southern type of grasshopper occasionally found around Vienna where the climate is favourable. The only thing I liked about my assignment was the fact that I had to look for *Mantis* eggs in the Wachau region, the most beautiful stretch of the Danube valley in Austria. While I hung about with nothing to do, waiting for my *Mantis* eggs to hatch, I became interested in the work of a fellow student who investigated the formation of pigment in fish. I was soon fascinated by the way minnows adapted their colour quickly to that of a light or dark background, a phenomenon based on rapid changes in the position of pigments within microscopic pigment cells embedded in their skin. Since I had myself been concerned with, admittedly somewhat different, shifts in pigment position in my first scientific investigation at the Physiological Institute, the matter interested me personally, being both novel and familiar at the same time.

Przibram, who did not believe in leading strings, let me follow my inclination. He drew my attention to an earlier paper by the French scientist Pouchet, who described how, on severing the *nervus sympathicus*, the tail of the fish behind the point of severance turns black. I repeated Pouchet's experiments, and discovered by accident that minnows suddenly go pale about 20 min. after they have been killed, and that in this condition the severance

FIG. 14.   Myself and my uncle Sigmund Exner in the Brunnwinkl "museum", *ca.* 1910.

of the nerve still had the same effect. When without any very clear design I moved the cut progressive farther up along the body, I had another surprise: for suddenly it was the front part of the fish that turned black. I completely forgot my *Mantis* eggs and studied the nervous pathways and nerve centres of colour changes. I had once more become absorbed in a problem of comparative physiology, and whenever I found myself at a loss I had only to take the familiar road to the Physiological Institute and ask the advice of my uncle Sigmund Exner. He thus became my teacher for a second time. After no more than a single term I was able to complete my investigation and submit it to Professor Grobben. Though he viewed with a certain suspicion whatever came from the Biological Institute, he accepted my work as a thesis, and I was thus able to present myself for the final, *viva voce*, examination towards the end of the winter term 1909/10.

I had chosen botany for my subsidiary subject. In place of the second subsidiary required in Germany, the Austrian statutes demanded an examination in philosophy. Most people prepared for this examination in a matter of weeks, guided by the advice of the examining Professor. Hence I, too, presented myself to Professor L. Müller with no more than a smattering of the subject, yet uncomfortably aware of the fact that of real philosophy I knew next to nothing. Müller's first and only question concerned the theory of evolution. He was opposed to Darwin's theory of natural selection, a fact which had secretly irritated me for a long time, for I was an enthusiastic Darwinian. Now I had an opportunity to give vent to this annoyance. Completely forgetting the situation, I started a long and bitter argument with the old Professor. I feared the worst, but Müller gave me "distinction", stating as his reason that I had expressed an opinion of my own.

For my main subject, zoology, I had worked very little, partly because I relied on what I had learned from Hertwig and partly because I had been busy with my colour-change experiments. Unfortunately, Grobben asked questions about matters I had not learned at Munich—very boring matters, I thought. It was touch and go, but I just scraped through. When I came home rather crestfallen and told my parents of the examination result, my mother said nothing. She just laughed. After that I did not worry either. I had my degree. That was all that mattered.

At that time it was the custom of Vienna University to organize university study tours in the Easter vacation which usually went into some part of the Mediterranean. Having just passed my finals, I joined the tour for Easter 1910 which took us to the Dalmatian coast. The University had chartered a roomy freighter, and by installing innumerable bunks had turned its holds into dormitories. Though the whole trip lasted no more than a week we saw and

experienced a great deal that is normally out of reach of the ordinary tourist in so short a time. A competent captain of the merchant
marine was in charge of navigation. He took his orders from the
Scientific Committee headed by the botanist E. von Wettstein and
the palaeobiologist O. Abel. We were accompanied by professors of
a great variety of disciplines, and each night experts would lecture
to us on the programme for the following day. There was plenty to
see and to admire on that lovely, deeply indented coastline of
Illyria (then, of course, still a part of Austria).

Highlights that stand out from the faded canvas
of my memories include the picturesque shores of
the lovely Bay of Kotor, the romantic old harbour
of Trau (Trogir), an excursion inland to the old
Mohammedan town of Mostar with its ancient
Roman bridge, a trip by torpedo boat to where the
Narenta emerges from the rock as a mighty river,
and a visit to the blue grotto of Busi (no less beautiful though less accessible than that of Capri).

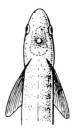

In the summer term I continued my experiments on the colour changes of fish at the Biological Research Station in the Prater, and during
that period I savoured for the first time the joy of

FIG. 15. Head of
a minnow with
frontal eye.

real discovery. I had observed that my minnows, even when both
their eyes had been removed, still reacted to light by a colour change:
they turned light in the dark and dark in the light. In order to find
out whether this reaction of the blind fish was due to an immediate
local effect of light on the pigment cells, I confined a blind minnow
in a glass container which fitted its body exactly. I then directed a
fine ray of light towards various parts of the skin, without success.
But when the small spot of light fell upon the forehead of the fish,
its whole body turned dark within a few seconds. On this very spot
there was a translucent patch (Fig. 15) like a window, exactly
corresponding to the frontal eye of lizards (an organ surrounded
by legend the function of which was, however, highly controversial).
But here there was no doubt. Of course I lost no time in reporting
my discovery to Sigmund Exner, who at first was rather sceptical.
Nevertheless he made the long journey to the Prater to see my
experiments, and was convinced.

Underneath that translucent window in the cranium of the minnow there is no rudimentary eye, but an elongated extension of the diencephalon, the epiphysis or pineal body. A histological analysis of this organ had revealed the presence of sensory cells. It appeared to serve as a third, very primitive eye. But to my disappointment a rudiment of light sensitivity remained even when the gland was removed. The whole area of the diencephalon appeared to be light-sensitive.

My pupil Ernst Scharrer was later able to demonstrate the light sensitivity of the diencephalon by a food-training technique. Blind minnows quickly learned to search for food after the frontal eye had been exposed to light. On this occasion Scharrer discovered the neurosecretory cells of the diencephalon, a discovery that launched him on to a field of research which was to become his life's work. But whether these striking light responses are mediated by sensory cells or by the hormone-secreting nerve cells discovered by Scharrer is something we still do not know.

Thinking back on those years I am filled with a bitter sense of self-reproach. My father showed the keenest interest in my early efforts at independent research of which he was unashamedly proud. I could not have given him greater pleasure than by letting him share the thoughts that occupied my mind from morning to night, the plans worked out in the evening for the experiments of the following day, the daily triumphs and setbacks—all the excitement and turmoil of my early development. Unfortunately, his eager interest made me feel embarrassed and inhibited, and I always remained reserved and silent in his presence. Though our personal relations were never troubled, I realized too late that I had missed an opportunity for repaying to a modest degree, albeit in a different coin, his unceasing solicitude for my welfare and career.

ASSISTANT AT THE ZOOLOGICAL
INSTITUTE, MUNICH

IT WAS pleasant to work at the Biological Research Station like a gentleman naturalist of old at my own pace and without outside pressures, but obviously this desirable state of affairs could not last very long, for I needed to earn money. Professor Hertwig had once asked me in passing whether I would be interested in a post at his Institute once I had passed my examinations, but as he had not mentioned the matter again after I had obtained my degree, I was afraid to approach him. Fortunately, I received about that time a letter from K. Heider offering me a job as assistant at the Zoological Institute, Innsbruck. This gave me a welcome opportunity to sound Hertwig, for Munich attracted me much more. I wrote him a letter, ostensibly asking his advice about Heider's offer. His reply was a great surprise to me. He discussed with complete detachment and in great detail the merits of the assistantships in Innsbruck and Munich, and asked me to choose without any consideration for him, guided only by my own preference. Joyfully, I decided for Munich. As I found out later, Hertwig at his end had been most surprised that I had never reacted to a letter of his offering me the job—a letter which he had composed in his mind but never actually written. This kind of thing happened to him more than once during the later years of his life.

Thus it came about that I returned to Munich in the autumn of 1910. The first thing I did as an assistant was to take part in the festivities that marked Richard Hertwig's sixtieth birthday, for which countless pupils, young and old, had assembled to do him homage. Two events stand out from the memories of that joyful and varied occasion.

One was the performance of a "Festival Play" by Richard Goldschmidt, satirizing with wit and good humour the so-called fertilization day at the Institute. Actually this was a very serious matter, for it was the day on which the members of the Minor Zoological Practical (mostly medical students and future biologists) were shown the penetration of the live eggs of sea urchins by sperm cells and the development of the free swimming larva (*Pluteus*) from the fertilized egg. Sea-urchin eggs were among Richard Hertwig's early loves, for on this material his brother Oscar had been the first both to observe and to interpret correctly the process of fertilization, and he himself had studied their development under normal and experimentally varied conditions. Their importance in this context lies in their transparency, which makes it possible to watch under the microscope the formation of the gut inside the embryo as clearly as the development of its exterior shape, and since the development takes place freely in water, a small dish of sea water is all that is required. It was natural that Hertwig should make use of this favourable material in order to demonstrate to his class such fundamental facts of life as fertilization and development of eggs in a complete sequence. For this purpose he arranged each term for some sea urchins to be sent from Trieste to Munich at the appropriate time. From the moment a telegram informed him that the consignment was under way, the whole Institute was in a state of excitement like a disturbed ant heap. Because there were only 2 hours available at the Practical in which to show all important stages of a development that in nature takes about 2 days, it was vital that the animals be handled with the utmost care in the few days which separated their arrival and the actual demonstration. Fertilizations had to be repeated according to a carefully timed schedule to ensure the correct sequence of stages for the day of demonstration. A great many things had to be kept in mind during these preparatory manipulations, and the utmost care was necessary if there were to be no hitch. Woe betide the young assistant who tended cultures of different stages with the same pipette and risked transferring an egg from one dish to another where it had no business to be! Hertwig had his eyes everywhere, and liked to do as much as he could himself. No effort was too great, no hour too late for him to guide and supervise the whole business.

This extreme solicitude of the Professor's, coupled with some barbed allusions to other persons and events, formed the main theme of the witty play that received a spirited performance on that memorable evening. Today the fertilization and development of live sea-urchin eggs belongs to the stock-in-trade of most zoological institutes, only we do not make quite so much fuss about it. I have to admit, however, that there is occasionally a gap where one of the stages is missing, something that was unthinkable in Hertwig's day.

The other highlight of the evening was the presentation of three stout volumes of essays in honour of Hertwig's sixtieth birthday by Theodor Boveri, his oldest pupil, who made a speech of truly classical beauty. The first volume was devoted to studies on cells and protozoa: the second contained papers on biology and phylogenic evolution, and the third reported an experimental research. This great variety in the work of his pupils reflected the versatility of Hertwig's genius. Nowadays contributions in honour of somebody or other are usually published in scientific journals just like any other papers, the only difference being a dedication at the top. Then they were actually published as a special volume and therefore, naturally, reached a much smaller public. Sigmund Exner rightly remarked at the time that these three volumes were a touching proof of the devotion inspired by Hertwig, since so many of his pupils were prepared to bury their brain children alive between their covers.

The festivities over, I settled down to the routine of an assistant's life compounded of manifold duties and stimulating opportunities. I now had to act as a teacher in the Major Practical where only yesterday I had sat as a learner. Paul Buchner, who was soon to become well known for his brilliant research on intercellular symbiosis, started work at the same time. Richard Goldschmidt, the chief assistant, took us both under his wing and initiated us on his daily rounds through the laboratory into the aims and methods of the course.

Naturally there were plenty of other duties apart from teaching in the Practical. But we had nevertheless enough time left for our own researches for Hertwig never expected his assistants to help with his own experiments. He also dealt with administration practically single-handed. In his slow, deliberate handwriting he not only drafted but wrote out the many memoranda and official requests that were unavoidable even then.

Every afternoon we, i.e. the assistants, students engaged on their theses, and graduate guests, would meet at tea-time in Goldschmidt's rooms, where conversation ranged widely over zoology, art, politics, and topical events. Goldschmidt was endowed with wide interests and a subtle humour. It was amazing how much time he managed to devote to us youngsters—simply being able to work with exceptional intensity at other times. On Ash Wednesday there would be beer and sausages at the Augustiner-Bräu before the Practical started at 11 a.m.; or on a balmy night in May we would all enjoy a bowl of punch in the open. His infectious enthusiasm induced us to play football together and to go on joint skiing excursions in the nearby mountains—so much less overrun than they are, alas! today. In these varied and informal social activities even I, though I am by nature reserved and unsociable, laid the foundation for some life-long friendships: with Richard Goldschmidt himself, and also with Doflein, P. Buchner, and O. Koehler, a colleague slightly younger than myself. Those were merry carefree years in that golden age before the First World War —its golden quality symbolized somehow by the glittering gold coins in which we regularly received one-half of our monthly stipend.

My scientific work had at that time (1911) taken an entirely new direction. The impulse came from C. von Hess, Director of the Munich Eye Clinic, to whom I shall always be grateful for his unintentional influence. On the basis of large-scale experiments with animals Hess had come to the conclusion that fish and all invertebrates were completely colour blind, a view which to me appeared incompatible with my own observations regarding the ability of fish to adapt themselves to the colour of their background. I tested this capacity in new experiments under conditions which precluded an explanation in terms other than those of colour recognition, and, in addition, obtained further information on the nature of colour vision in fish by training some individuals to respond to coloured objects.

The publications of these findings gave rise to an open conflict with von Hess which developed into a heated and acrimonious feud continuing over many years in connection with further papers of mine on colour vision in bees and other animals. It was not easy for me, a beginner, to prevail against a scientist of international repute. To my great disappointment, von Hess was not prepared to look at my experiments which, if his theories were right, could not possibly succeed. I was furious at his attempts to discredit me and to twist my statements so that they would agree with his ideas, and I did not mince words in my rejoinders. This earned me a rebuke from Hertwig who reproached me, not without justification, for using immoderate language towards a man of von Hess's age and eminence. In the matter itself he was, however, on my side absolutely. He personally attended all my experiments in place of Hess, signed the records, and permitted me to publish them over his name. As it turned out, I was eventually proved right and I soon ceased to harbour any rancour towards my stubborn opponent. But who can tell whether my life would have taken as happy and successful a turn without this early controversy which attracted the notice of fellow scientists?

Easter 1911 found me once more in the Mediterranean spending nearly 2 months at the Zoological Research Station at Naples. I was anxious to continue my investigations on colour adaptation and colour vision in fish on some of the marvellously colourful species of the marine fauna. The "Statione Zoologica", a large white building standing amidst old trees on the shores of the famous bay, was admirably equipped for the research I had in mind. But even after all these years I feel a slight shiver when I think of the set-up of my experiments. In one of these I wanted to keep my fish for several weeks in light of different colours. To this end the aquaria were placed in slightly larger glass containers filled with colour solutions. Sea water was continually piped into and drained from the aquaria through openings in their tightly fitting lids, for otherwise my fish would soon have died of suffocation. Some of my colour solutions were highly toxic. If ever one of the siphons had become clogged, the poisonous liquid would have mixed with the sea-water which was kept in constant circulation by pumping. The nightmare of seeing all the station's marine animals dead or dying made me sometimes get up in the middle of the night to check the siphons. I do not know to this day whether Reinhard Dohrn, the director, permitted this arrangement because he trusted me to be careful or because he thought that the poison, even if it should get into the sea water, would be so diluted in the vast ramifications of the station's pipe system as to be of no serious consequence. I certainly assumed that he trusted me, and tried to justify his confidence by the utmost vigilance. As it happened, I was lucky. Nothing went wrong.

The Zoological Station was founded in 1874 by Reinhard's father, Anton Dohrn, in the face of great opposition and untold difficulties. It was the first of its kind and has served as a model for many later foundations. Dohrn's idea was to provide for the study of the animal and plant life of the sea—so much more varied and so much older than that of freshwater habitats. The pioneers who had first studied marine life from the sea-shore had been seriously handicapped by the lack of those facilities which only a well-equipped research laboratory can provide. While Dohrn was still struggling to get his plan accepted, old Professor Ehrenberg of Berlin delivered himself of the opinion that, given the equipment and the staffing envisaged, there would be little left to investigate for botanists or zoologists in the Bay of Naples 5 or 10 years hence. Dohrn saw more clearly. Today no less than at the beginning (perhaps even more so) scientists from all civilized countries work together at Naples all the year round and there is still plenty of work for all to do. This permanent international gathering of biologists owes its existence to a brilliant idea of Dohrn's. As a means of financing his station he hit upon the plan of inducing the governments of the chief civilized countries to rent working space at the laboratory for the benefit of their citizens. As a second source of income he created a display aquarium within the station, thus inducing ordinary people to contribute to the upkeep of biological research while being themselves enthralled by the wonders of the deep.

Looking up from my desk my gaze would rest upon the blue bay of Naples with the incomparable silhouette of the isle of Capri on the horizon, framed by the Sorrento peninsula and Cape Misenum and surmounted by the smoke clouds emitted by old Mt. Vesuvius. There was also the well-equipped library, adorned with beautiful murals by the hand of Dohrn's friend H. von Marées, and if for once I got tired of working, the Museum of Naples, the excavations of Pompeii, the sea, and the strange countryside provided exhilarating recreation for hours or days.

I liked it all so much that I went back there again in the Easter vacations of 1912 and 1913.

In 1912 my friend O. Koehler was there with me. We shared a room high up on Mt. Vomero, with a splendid view of the gulf. Being older and more experienced, I was able to be of use to him in his work. He, on the other hand, knew a great deal more about art and the classics than I did. What better chance could there be of filling the gaps in my education than the presence of these unforgettable "visual aids"? Even more we enjoyed the enchanting landscape which surrounds the art treasures of the past. For me its beauty and grandeur surpassed everything made by the hand of man. We climbed Mt. Vesuvius together, and after we had successfully eluded the importunate crowd of guides (and paid for our independence by losing our way several times) we doubly enjoyed the vast panorama spread out before us and the uncanny manifestations of the volcano itself close at hand. Another time when taking a walk towards Cape Misenum late one evening, we stepped out of a dense wood on to a sandy shore bathing in the light of the moon. There, to our surprise and joy, we suddenly came upon a herd of wild boar rooting for *frutti di mare* at the water's edge and looking in the pale light of the moon like so many demons from hell. We had strayed into an enclosed deer park without noticing. Once we took a small cheap steamer, patronized almost exclusively by the local population, to visit Capri for the day. On the way back we ran into a gale. The deck was crowded and I was soon surrounded on all sides by the *spaghetti con pomidoro* my fellow passengers had obviously enjoyed consuming on the island. Though I am normally a good sailor, the sight of the storm-tossed spaghetti very nearly induced me to sacrifice to Neptune myself. The experience taught me always to seek the windward side of a boat deck under similar circumstances. The raging sea was, however, a marvellous sight. After such escapist episodes we worked with redoubled zest and application. I have always felt that scientific research thrives best in beautiful and harmonious surroundings.

LECTURESHIP AND FURTHER WORK
AS ASSISTANT IN MUNICH

THE outcome of my research at Munich and Naples was a paper entitled "Colour adaptation in fishes". Hertwig suggested that I submit it to the Faculty to obtain admission as *Privatdozent* (lecturer without stipend) at Munich University. In March 1912, 2 years after taking my degree, I achieved this coveted status, then, as now, the first rung on the German academic ladder.

To do so it was not sufficient to present a paper of scientific merit; there was also a "Colloquium", a *viva voce* examination before and by the assembled Faculty at which one's general scientific knowledge was put to the test. Once over that hurdle one had to deliver a test lecture on a set subject and subsequently to defend some scientific propositions or "theses" put forward therein which custom required to be somewhat daring so that the attackers would have something to pitch into.

The Colloquium was then, and still is, the stiffest part of the whole procedure, for the candidate cannot foresee what sort of questions the examiners will take it into their heads to ask, nor what disciplines will be touched upon in his ordeal, which lasts a full hour. In my case most of the subjects were interesting enough and all was plain sailing until Professor Rothpletz, a palaeontologist, started to ask about some fossil sharks' teeth. Fortunately, no one else of those present knew anything about that subject, and therefore my failure to answer his question did not do me any great harm.

The test lecture then was rather different from what it is today. Nowadays the candidate himself proposes three topics from which the Faculty chooses one. He is therefore sure of a subject with which he is reasonably familiar, and he knows several weeks in advance what he may have to talk about. In my time it was the Faculty that set the task, and the subject was communicated only

52

3 days before the date of the lecture. The choice lay, of course, with the Professor concerned, and I knew that Hertwig had strict views on such matters and would not let me off lightly. True enough, he selected from the field of comparative anatomy a problem on the head segments of vertebrates, which gave me quite a headache in the 3 short days at my disposal.

I consider these surprise tactics a better test of a candidate's ability than the present method. You had to prove that you were able to inform yourself rapidly from the available literature on any subject, however remote, and give a reasonable account of matters with which 3 days earlier you may not have been familiar. This, after all, is likely to happen more than once in a lecturer's future career!

My father came specially from Vienna to be present on this momentous occasion and hear me deliver my first lecture. I had carefully written down in manuscript what I was going to say. Goldschmidt, an old hand, advised me not to rely on my manuscript but rather to use keywords written on slips of paper— excellent advice which I have followed ever since, but which on that occasion I disregarded with almost disastrous results. I had not in the least imagined what the situation was going to be. The charts with the illustrations I needed were hung at the back and sides of the dais and while I was trying to explain some point with the help of these charts, a yawning chasm separated me from the desk on which my manuscript lay. The result was that at some tricky point I lost my thread completely and even after I had unobtrusively worked my way back to the desk at last, I could not find my place on the page. Somehow I managed to muddle through without the audience noticing. Goldschmidt, of course, had noticed all right, and I had to accept his (privately administered) "I told you so" with as good a grace as I could muster.

After the lecture there followed a long discussion in which Hertwig, aided by some pugnacious members of the audience, vigorously attacked the whole tenor of my argument and the propositions I had formulated. A fierce battle was joined, but it all ended amicably. Hertwig on such occasions exercised his rare gift for guiding a discussion to a conclusion which satisfied the honour of both contestants.

There was almost a glut in new *Privatdozenten* at the time. On the very same day Paul Buchner, who had been a fellow undergraduate and my colleague as assistant, was also promoted, and very soon we were joined by Hans Kupelwieser, a member of a wealthy Austrian family who was able to devote his life to our science without the need for a paid appointment, a happy state of affairs almost unknown in our country today. Moreover, his father, Dr. Carl Kupelwieser, had built for him in 1906 a private hydrobiological research station on the shores of Lake Lunz in Lower Austria, destined to play an increasingly important role in creative research and in biological teaching. When private fortunes melted away after the First World War, the institute was transferred to a trust, *Biologische Station Lunz*, which had been founded in 1923 chiefly with funds from the Kaiser Wilhelm Gesellschaft (now the Max Planck Gesellschaft) in Germany and the Austrian Academy of Sciences.

We three newly fledged (private) lecturers were on the best of terms. The 2 years which were to be allowed to us before the outbreak of the First World War were for us a period of creative work and mutual stimulation. There was nothing of that secretiveness sometimes found in institutes where everybody seems to fear another might filch his discoveries. We enjoyed frank and full exchanges of information about our work—finished or not—and such exchanges of ideas were not restricted to zoology alone. Every Wednesday night a Biological Club of zoologists, botanists, physiologists, anatomists, palaeontologists, and other scientists met in the library of the Zoological Institute. The representatives of the various disciplines were called in rotation to report on the most interesting developments in their respective fields of research. Discussions were free, informal, and to the point. Frequently they ended late at night in harmless gaiety at some neighbouring beer garden. The club, which had been founded by Franz Doflein, originally did not admit lecturers or professors in order that even the youngest members might feel free to talk without fear or inhibition. When Doflein became a private lecturer, the barrier was moved up a step, and when he became an assistant professor, full professors only were barred. This rule was never waived. For when Doflein achieved a chair, he left Munich.

In Brunnwinkl I had a few bee-hives. The region is not very suitable for bee-keeping and honey crops were few and far between. But I was interested in bees for other reasons and started my first experiments with them in the summer of 1912. The theory of their total colour-blindness provoked my opposition. An unbiased observer was much more inclined to believe the theories of the flower biologists who thought that the bright colours of petals served to make the inflorescences conspicuous to bees and other pollinating insects; that they were, in fact, colourful inn signs announcing where nectar was to be had, the guests paying for their meal by the service of pollination. Was it credible that this relationship was falsely regarded as the perfect example of mutual adaptation, and that the glory of the flowers should be nothing but a meaningless display before the eyes of colour-blind insects?

The colour-blindness of fish had turned out to be a fallacy. I decided to tackle this new problem with the same methods of food training that had been successful in my earlier work. The bees proved to be excellent pupils. It was only necessary to feed them sugar water for a short while on, say, blue squares of cardboard for them to associate the colour blue with food. And if later a blue square, without food, was placed amidst a collection of squares in all shades of grey from white to black, the bees would ignore all other squares and alight on the blue in search of the sugar water they had been led to expect there. By so doing they gave a clear answer to the question whether they see blue as a distinct colour. For, to a colour-blind eye, blue is identical with a grey of a certain intensity, and if the bees were devoid of colour vision they would confound the blue to which they had been trained with that particular shade of grey.

This simple method not only served to prove that bees had colour vision, it also enabled me to elucidate various aspects of its nature which agreed in a most gratifying manner with certain peculiarities of floral hues.

If some new piece of research goes well, it usually produces far more new questions than answers. I had therefore planned a great many new training experiments when autumn put an end to my research for the time being. In the summer of 1913 I was very anxious to bring the investigation to a successful conclusion, and

E

therefore I sometimes trained my bees to colours at as many as four different places at once, rushing round from one to the next the whole day long in a frenzied effort to keep them all going. This stage I could just manage on my own. But for the experiments proper it was necessary after due preparation for all bees alighting on the various cardboard squares to be carefully counted. For this I needed helpers, and the members of our family group rose cheerfully to the task. My two grey-bearded uncles, the Professors Franz and Sigmund Exner, volunteered at once, and I could not have wished for better or more reliable observers. But they could not cope with all the work, so that my cousins and some permanent guests were pressed into service outright or made to remain at hand rather than go for walks. About these people I did not feel quite so sure, and I used to test the trustworthiness of new recruits by secretly checking their results. I remember one young law student whose records were consistently wrong. He had to be dropped at once. Looking back, I should not be at all surprised if he had done it on purpose.

While the experiments were in full swing and at their most exciting, a letter from Hertwig in Munich hit me like a bolt out of the blue. Hertwig was usually not difficult about leave, especially if he knew that it was well employed, but he insisted that at least one of his assistants should be in Munich during the vacation as the laboratory work of the senior students did, of course, go on. Up to then I had generally been lucky, for either Goldschmidt or Buchner had been staying in Munich anyway in connection with their own research work. That year, however, Buchner had gone to the Naples Station. So, when Goldschmidt was taking a few weeks' leave, Hertwig, to my horror and dismay, ordered me to come back at once. I had no choice but to obey, but once in Munich I tried with all the powers of persuasion I could muster to convince him that my presence there was quite unnecessary and that the continuation of my Brunnwinkl experiments was far more important. The senior students were, in fact, in no need of help, and I completely failed to see the force of Hertwig's other arguments. He, however, was concerned with the principle of the thing. There was a long and acrimonious interview at the end of which we both had tears in our eyes, but he remained adamant. However—only till the next day. Then he sent me back to Brunnwinkl, having charged one of the senior students to deputize for me while Goldschmidt was away. In the conflict between his strict sense of duty and discipline and his kind heart, the latter had once more gained the upper hand. The investigation on the bees was brought to a successful conclusion. I shall never cease to be grateful to him for this.

At that time my feud with von Hess was at its height. Our assertions flatly contradicted each other, and readers of our papers frequently were at a loss whom to believe. These were the circumstances which induced me to announce as my contribution to the Meeting of the German Zoological Society held at Freiburg during Whitsun 1914 a "demonstration providing experimental evidence for the existence of colour vision in animals supposed to be colour-blind". Unfortunately, the tap water of Freiburg did not agree with the trained fish I had brought with me from Munich, making them sick and useless for my demonstration. For a time it looked as if the bees, too, would let me down, for because of the local abundance of natural food that spring the Freiburg bees were just not interested in the honey I had laid out as a bait. At the very last moment I discovered some bees gathering water from lettuce plants in the institute caretaker's freshly watered vegetable garden. With great patience and cunning I managed to convert them to the sugar water offered on the experimental table. This saved my day, for when it came to the demonstration in the garden of the Freiburg Institute the bees behaved exactly as I wanted them to and did what, as colour-blind creatures, they were not supposed to be doing. An unrehearsed sequel made the demonstration even more impressive. For I later showed some of the plates for a forthcoming publication on the colour vision of bees, which reproduced the experimental set-up on a small scale, i.e. four sets of blue squares surrounded by squares of the same size in various shades of grey. As I had omitted to refill the little food dishes on the experimental table, my blue-trained bees buzzed about searching for food. The moment I unfolded the plates bees alighted on each of the little blues squares as if by command, although these squares were so small that their bodies covered them completely. This was entirely unexpected and absolutely convincing.

One might have thought that my scientific successes would have made me confident and happy. But while they occurred, these events looked quite different from their appearance in retrospect. The road to assured results in experimental research is a long and arduous one, paved more often than not with tedious search for suitable methods, with errors and false starts leading nowhere, with doubts about the right procedure and worries about sources of error one might have overlooked, with disappointments and setbacks of every conceivable kind. It is a matter of temperament how one takes these things. Then and later I was often depressed and downcast for weeks if my work did not progress satisfactorily, and considered myself a failure. For many years I thought of each new investigation that this would be the last time I had any ideas, and I have never completely overcome this feeling. Another thing that worried me when I started my academic career was whether I would ever be able to think up interesting subjects should students ask me to write their theses under me. And I would fear that even if something were to come out of my research, it would never be anything really useful.

When I was in these morbid moods I was sometimes cheered by one of Wilhelm Busch's caustic little verses:

| When I was young,
I was modest and raw
and mostly held other
people in awe. | Früher, da ich unerfahren
Und bescheidner war als heute,
Hatten meine höchste Achtung
Andre Leute. |
| When later I met
other donkeys galore,
I esteemed others less
and myself – so much more. | Später traf ich auf der Weide
Ausser mir noch mehre Kälber
Und nun schätz ich sozusagen
Erst mich selber. |

This little gem of irreverent wisdom was my lifeline once when depression threatened to swamp me.

Sometimes it was my mother who knew how to comfort me and who with a few strokes of the brush brought back the colour into my vision of the future. One of her letters, written during the early period of my assistantship with Hertwig, is so characteristic that I want to cite it here.

My dear Karlinchen,

Only stupid people never doubt themselves. An historical fact. No artist or scientist worth his salt will escape such moods in his period of development. I myself have experienced this struggle at close range with your uncle Adolf, the most brilliant of my four brothers. If you chafe under the lack of independence, think that your father worked alongside his master Billroth for many a year, that uncle Schiga* was for 20 years assistant to Brücke, and uncle Serafin† likewise spent all his youth as assistant to his teacher Lang: And yet *you* insist on pulling yourself up by your own boot straps as it were? Well darling, really! I am also very surprised that you are so anxious to serve humanity at all costs—this is a new trait in you. Any work you do, steadily and devotedly, will be for humanity in the end. It is, of course, hardly ever possible to say in advance whether anything is likely to come out of such work as yours, or what it may lead to, but each step forward towards a better understanding of nature may give rise to unthought-of new discoveries. Surely you know that. Or have you suddenly got disappointed with zoology? Is that the rub? I do hope that you have begun to see the sun once more through all this murk—you said yourself you would probably be on top of the world again in a week's time. Do let me hear from you even if it is only a post card!

Frau Richter‡ told me in a letter that you had been to Tegernsee and that you had joined in the tobogganing as if you had done it all your life, whereas in fact it had been your very first ride. Well then, if all else fails here is something you can fall back on. . . .

Affectionately
Your old M.

---

* The physiologist Sigmund Exner.
† The physicist Franz Serafin Exner.
‡ My brother Otto's mother-in-law.

INTERLUDE AT THE RUDOLFINERHAUS, 1914–1918

THE 29 June, the feast of SS. Peter and Paul, was a holiday in catholic Bavaria. In the year 1914 I took this opportunity to make a short visit to Brunnwinkl, where my mother and other members of my family were already installed for the summer. I arrived on the afternoon of the 28th. Just when we were all sitting together, drinking coffee and chatting pleasantly, the news came that the heir-apparent, Archduke Franz Ferdinand, had been assassinated at Sarajevo. He had not been much liked in Austria and there had been grave misgivings about his impending reign. I recall that some of the people present thought his sudden death might even have removed a possible danger from the future of our country. Fate decreed otherwise. A month later we were at war.

Since I had not been a conscript because of my poor eyesight, I was not immediately affected by the general call-up. Politically and emotionally the struggle between the peoples of Europe had no meaning for me.

Soon our Institute at Munich was empty. Even those who did not enlist could not concentrate on zoology in times like these. Hertwig released me and thought I should go back to my own country. So I returned to Brunnwinkl and, since in the first flush of warlike enthusiasm there appeared to be an excess of willing helpers for whom there was no work to do, I took up a series of experiments with my bees which I had already prepared. Not for long though. Only a few weeks later the form of my war work was decided for me. It was to take me to the Rudolfinerhaus in Vienna.

Theodor Billroth, a leading member of the Vienna medical school and professor at Vienna University from 1867 to his death in 1894, had gained first-hand experience of the surgery of the battlefield in 1870. Recognizing that it was essential to train a corps of women who would be able to nurse the wounded and to withstand the rigours of war before the actual need arose, he founded a surgical hospital incorporating a nurses' training school, the Rudolfinerhaus in the Vienna suburb of Döbling.

As soon as war broke out, the Rudolfinerhaus was turned into a military hospital. One of the departmental surgeons was my brother Otto, my senior by 9 years. During the "Balkan war" of 1912 he had been sent to the front with a detachment of his nurses and gained first-hand experience of war-time surgery. He was now made superintendent of the whole hospital. Though, ardent and adventurous as he was, he often longed to go to the front and practise first aid there, he found the task that had been entrusted to him the more rewarding in the long run. For only at a base hospital could one hope to apply the whole armoury of medicine to the task of setting the wounded on the road to recovery without losing them prematurely.

At the end of August 1914 the erstwhile model hospital did not look a bit like its old peace-time self. The number of beds had been raised from 100 to 400 by putting emergency beds and even palliasses into all the corridors. In order to make room for new admissions, yet keep an eye on lesser casualties and convalescents who did not require full-time medical attention, nursing facilities were arranged in nearby private houses. These amounted to another 600 beds in the end, so that the whole establishment had ten times the number of beds as in peace-time. And the patients who came were not just cases of appendicitis or bladder trouble. The transports of seriously wounded came straight to us from the eastern battlefields after 2 or 3 days of gruelling journey. All too many were in a pitiful state with dirty, suppurating wounds, covered with vermin, and frequently suffering also from infectious diseases. Everything about their reception had to be improvised; at that time there were no delousing stations or other auxiliary services which later were to become routine.

Moreover, many of the doctors and nurses who had been available for the care of 100 peace-time patients had been called to the front and had been replaced by inadequate personnel or not at all.

In these circumstances my brother let me know that he needed help. Would I come? From this request there arose an intimate working partnership between us which lasted right through the war without a discord. At first I worked on a voluntary basis, but after about 2 years I was employed by the Red Cross. I cannot describe what my brother accomplished in these years. He never allowed himself a single day's rest. The work never ceased for a minute, keeping the hospital, and its superintendent, in a state of perpetual tension day and night. And though in some ways things gradually became slightly easier and better organized, any relief this might have afforded him was offset by a directive issued to the reception centre for incoming transports to the effect that only severe cases were henceforth to be sent to the "Rudolfinerhaus". This directive arose from a visit of inspection by the Chief of the Medical Staff. It implied high praise, but it added to the strain. I found myself the only layman in a fanatically busy crowd of doctors and nurses faced with an indescribable agglomeration of human misery. In the beginning the main thing was to tackle any job that came along. At first this meant shifting beds, affixing fever charts, helping in reception and similar chores, but soon my activities became more regularized. I learned to take X-ray photographs, became a theatre anaesthetist, and helped with the dressing of wounds.

As in the first months of the war the wounded came to us without any previous screening, we often received cases suspected of dysentery, typhoid, or cholera. In the overcrowded condition of our hospital such cases presented a terrible danger. To obtain certainty through bacteriological tests, samples of blood and excreta had to be sent to a laboratory from which we could at best expect an answer in 4 to 5 days, and such delay might easily prove extremely serious. On the other hand, we hated sending to an infection hospital cases that badly needed surgical treatment.

On my suggestion we established our own bacteriological laboratory at the hospital. It started functioning towards the end of November 1914 in a roomy cellar put at our disposal. By then I had acquired the necessary, and of necessity very one-sided, special knowledge at the Institute of Hygiene. As we made our own culture media, our costs were low. Work there was in plenty.

The laboratory on the premises proved to be a very useful adjunct to the hospital right through the war. The fact that I was able to diagnose rapidly the few cases of cholera and the rather more numerous ones of dysentery and typhoid among the great mass of suspects gave me great satisfaction. This close contact between laboratory and wards was particularly valuable in the early stages when all was confusion and muddle. Later, when the base hospitals were no longer inundated with infectious diseases, the laboratory was chiefly employed for other purposes which did not take up so much of my time.

Gradually I transferred my activities more and more into the wards themselves. Towards the end of the war I was in charge of a department of 70 beds for which my brother was officially responsible. I had learned a great deal from him, though my medical training was, of necessity, completely oriented towards war-time surgery. Within this field I was, however, given the opportunity of performing many quite difficult operations, including amputations above the knee—though naturally under strict medical supervision. I became particularly interested in bullet fractures of the thigh and leg, on which I published a major paper jointly with my brother. The direct alleviation of human suffering was for me a new and wonderful aspect of life, and for some time I seriously considered taking up medicine again and saying goodbye to zoology. My brother was very much in favour of this plan, but it was nevertheless largely due to him that it came to nothing in the end. During the war he insisted repeatedly that I should go to Brunnwinkl in the summer for a few weeks' leave. Once there I realized that I had been famished for the company of animals, and invariably the first thing I did was to get down to my bees and my experiments on their sense of smell. Once again, food training proved a successful method and I was able to elucidate some interesting relationships in this almost totally unexplored field. Immersing myself thus completely in the delightful world of bees and flowers was for me the best form of relaxation. But it also meant that zoology had renewed her hold over me—and in the end she was to prove the stronger force in my life.

Actually, zoology came occasionally to my aid during the years of merciless slogging at the hospital. In the spring of 1915 we were very worried about typhus. Because this dangerous disease is spread by lice a reception hut had been built where the wounded were cleaned and their dressings changed to avoid introducing these insect vectors into the hospital itself. There my "expert zoologist's" eye was much in demand to make sure that not a single louse was being overlooked. Often, of course, you could not possibly miss them. Never again have I seen such masses of vermin as with these transports from the front. The lice seemed to have a preference for the padding inside plaster dressings and these had therefore to be taken off and renewed, without exception.

One other tenuous link remained between my work and my proper calling. All through the war the Rudolfinerhaus not only continued to function as a training school for nurses but did so on an extended scale. My brother did most of the teaching, which added considerably to his work load, while I provided a little variety by lecturing on biology. In addition I gave a few evening lectures on bacteriology to trainee and trained nurses alike, in which I tried to explain why the rigorous precautions they had been taught so insistently were necessary if spread of disease germs was to be avoided. Out of this course there grew a little book, *Six Lectures on Bacteriology for Nurses*, the compilation of which led to an unforeseen development. We were in the middle of the war. I was 30 years old and had more than once lost my heart completely, but in every case a gulf had separated me from the object of my dreams. Now I felt myself once more attracted. This time the object of my admiration was a certain nurse Dorothee, a trainee who had been working in my department but who to my dismay had been transferred to a distant pavilion. I neither knew nor cared that her real name was Margarethe Mohr (Fig. 16) nor that her father was a well-known bookseller and publisher. I was only concerned with the problem of how to become better acquainted, for the hectic work in the wards had offered precious little opportunity. Suddenly I had a brainwave. For my little book I would need a few illustrations; I went straight to nurse Dorothee in that distant pavilion and asked her point blank whether she could draw. Her immediate answer was "No". Here her superior, who happened to overhear the conversation, cut in and said: "Don't stand there playing the coy country-lass—of course you can!" For she knew that before the war this particular nurse had for many years been studying sculpture with Professor Kauffungen.

Admittedly, this had been rather different from drawing the portraits of bacteria, but I managed to convince her that the latter task was really much easier. From that day onward she would come to my laboratory every evening (duty permitting) to work there until late into the night on the illustrations for my little book. No one

Fig. 16.   Margarethe Mohr.

would guess, looking at them, that they had been instrumental in uniting two people for life.

My sister-in-law, Jenny, also worked at the hospital most days from morning to night as her husband's faithful helpmate. They had therefore taken a flat close by and let me share it. They obviously had no idea what was in the wind when I brought nurse Dorothee along for supper one evening under some pretext or other, and my brother slightly raised his eyebrows in surprise. But presently he and his guest vied with each other in hunting and fishing stories, and the evening passed very pleasantly.

Soon, however, our happy moments were to be clouded by the serious illness of my father. Within a short time his condition deteriorated, and on 24 May 1917 he ended a life of unceasing activity and constant solicitude for the welfare of his family. His deathbed was wreathed in richly flowering branches of may from our garden. I feel happy in the thought that he knew my future wife before he died and that he found pleasure in her delightful personality. But I often grieve that I cannot now tell him of this or that scientific achievement. How pleased he would have been!

Those were dark times—in more than one respect. Yet, now that we had found each other we felt we did not want to wait. On 20 July 1917 Margarethe and I were married in the village of Hinterbrühl near Vienna. I was granted a few weeks' leave. Our honeymoon took us to Wildalpen in Styria where my wife had spent some of the happiest days of her life in the summer residence of the Thimigs, a famous family of actors. Yet though it was beautiful there, I longed to get to my beloved Brunnwinkl. Probably because I had got so used to constant hard work through all those years I could not stand inactivity even as a newly wed. I believe my wife has never quite forgiven me for the fact that in the weeks that followed I was completely absorbed in my bees and made her wash the innumerable little dishes I needed for my scent training. When my brother heard about my behaviour, he wrote to his former pupil and present sister-in-law: "I am letting Karl have another week's holiday. If he does not take you for at least two decent walks you had better divorce him on the spot!" It appears that I fulfilled the condition. At any rate we were not divorced, neither then nor later.

We took up our married life together in my late father's professional suite in the Josefstädterstrasse, and there our first child was born to us in May 1918. There, in the large room that served as our bedroom and sitting room, the former nurse Dorothee would lie in bed, a picture of contented motherhood, while I sat at my desk, after a long day at the hospital, writing a lengthy paper on the bees' sense of smell and enveloping mother and baby daughter in clouds of cigar smoke.

We lived in my mother's house for over a year, and both of us treasure the memory of this experience.

The war came to an end. Work at the Rudolfinerhaus grew less, whereas work at the Zoological Institute at Munich increased as many demobilized former students, most of them war invalids, wished to continue their studies. After a break of 4 years, I therefore returned to my job as Assistant and Lecturer at the Institute—feeling distinctly poorer in many respects and conscious of the fact that a way of life had gone for ever. But one thing I had gained: a beloved wife. And on the day our little Hannerl for the first time crawled enterprisingly about the room, trailing a wet nappy behind her which traced the pattern of her progress on the polished floor, I thought of something my mother had once said to me some 15 years earlier. The whole scene had deeply imprinted itself on my memory as youthful experiences sometimes do: I was standing in front of my aquarium, in rapt contemplation of some newly hatched baby fish of my macropod couple when she remarked: "An even greater joy will be yours one day, when you will be watching your own brood grow up."

All our savings, which we had dutifully put into war loan were, of course, lost by inflation. But up to a point this proved to be a blessing in disguise. Since we had no money to buy furniture for our home, my mother and my in-laws let us have some beautiful early-nineteeth-century pieces they could spare, so that wherever we went in later life we always were surrounded by lovely familiar things which meant "home" to us in foreign parts.

BACK TO ZOOLOGY

FINDING accommodation in Munich was not going to be easy. So I first went alone to scout for a suitable billet. With luck I managed to find a flat on the fifth floor of No. 6 Gedonstrasse, in the pleasant suburb of Schwabing. From its windows there was a beautiful view of a magnificent rose garden. Unfortunately, my wife seemed less interested in the view from the front than in the kitchen at the back, which can perhaps best be described by the fact that our successor in the flat, a photographer by trade, used it as a darkroom. We also managed to find a woman willing to "oblige" for a few hours each day, something which at that time was probably even more difficult to come by than a flat. Admittedly, when we found our treasure using the slop pail for a mixing bowl, our pride of possession was slightly diminished. Such were the early joys and tribulations of keeping house.

In the political field the tribulations greatly outweighed the joys. The revolution had shattered the whole fabric of law and order which all of us had taken for granted since our childhood days. It was impossible to foresee when and in what form the situation would stabilize itself. At first, things went from bad to worse. The murder of Kurt Eisner by Count Arco gave a renewed impetus to the radical elements, leading to the proclamation of a soviet republic and the "dictatorship of the proletariat" in Bavaria. Food was scarce. Fierce-looking fellows with red armlets and rifles slung across their shoulders patrolled the streets. It was dangerous to show oneself in the street decently dressed. Those who were reasonably well off feared for their belongings.

The elegant house where we had our attic rooms and the one adjoining belonged to Professor L. Quidde, a well-known politician and pacifist. He himself was hardly ever at home. The pacifism of his vivacious, musical wife expressed itself most strongly in a limitless love for animals. When we played sonatas together the

68

mice would dance a minuet on the floor. They ruined the carpets and the professor's library, but Mrs. Quidde could not bear the thought of traps. Instead she fed them with bread in the vain hope that this would divert their appetite from more valuable pabulum. Her all-embracing love did, however, draw the line at Spartakists (members of a powerful left-wing semi-military organization). She lived in fear of one of those "commissions" which were then in the habit of searching and ransacking the flats of the well-to-do. She therefore called a meeting of all male inhabitants of both houses at her sister's flat next door to discuss possible measures of defence. At the appointed time the whole company was there—except Mrs. Quidde herself. The lengthy discussions held while we waited clearly showed how confused people were at the time. A young man suggested in all seriousness that we should throw paper bags filled with water out of the window should a commission appear at our front door. The "bombs" would burst and frighten the reds away! At long last Mrs. Quidde appeared. Her reason for being late was really the funniest part of this tragicomic afternoon: she had been held up by a group of communists who had searched her flat! However, she had been neither murdered nor robbed.

The troubles lasted for several weeks. Then, one day, the news that the liberators were standing outside the city spread like wildfire through our suburb. When I got to the nearby Leopoldstrasse a crowd of cheering people lined the pavements to greet the troops which Colonel von Epp had collected for the overthrow of the dictatorship and which he now led towards the city. After the rabble that had been in control, the mounted officers and their men, all clad in smart uniforms and behaving with perfect discipline, presented a heart-warming sight.

Things did not, however, go quite so smoothly as one might have hoped at the outset. Soon there were shots from windows and attics and it took quite a while before order was finally restored.

We stayed in Munich for $2\frac{1}{2}$ years. Soon we had to look for another flat as an addition to the family was expected. By the time the baby was born—another girl whom we named Maria—we had found what we wanted. The publisher and bookseller Paul Oldenbourg let us have some rooms in his spacious flat not far from our first lodgings in Schwabing. It was not long before we were received right into the bosom of his patriarchal family. For the landlord-and-tenant relationship soon blossomed into a friendship for life. Not only in those early days of our married life, but even more so during a subsequent stay in Munich when we had to go through a difficult and worrying time, Helene Oldenbourg was truly like a mother to us. Helene's friendship and understanding gave much-needed comfort and moral support to my wife when, during the days of the Third Reich, she was about to despair of life and of mankind.

At that earlier period we are talking of, political events seemed to me so much a natural consequence of the lunacy of the war that they did not impress themselves on my memory, partly, no doubt, because I immersed myself at once in my work with redoubled energy.

In January 1919, soon after I had resumed my post of Assistant, I was made an Assistant Professor and a year later I was asked to lecture on comparative physiology. In addition to the lectures I also conducted a practical on that subject, rather a new departure at that time. The innovation was very popular with the students and gave me, too, a great deal of satisfaction.

A few years earlier physiology, i.e. the science of the organs and their functions, and hence truly the science of the life of organisms, had been entirely bound up with human medicine. The only reason for animal experiments in medical schools was the impossibility of carrying out such experiments on human beings. It might have been expected that zoologists would use their familiarity with the entire animal kingdom to found a science of comparative physiology after the model of comparative anatomy. Yet probably because they were too absorbed in morphological studies of the endless varieties of known forms and, besides, lacked experience in the method of physiological experiments, this new branch of zoology was pioneered by physiologists working in medical faculties who possessed the necessary methodological skills.

True, the older literature does contain some records of early attempts in this direction. In the eighteenth century, Lazzaro Spallanzani made his famous experiments on the orientation of bats. In 1891 Sigmund Exner published his *Physiology of the*

Compound Eyes of Crustaceans and Insects, a classic of comparative physiology. Soon after the turn of the century Albrecht Bethe showed how the study of the nervous systems of lower animals could throw light on the functioning of the human nervous system. Hans Winterstein made fundamental experiments on the respiration of aquarian animals. Alois Kreidl elucidated by a classical experiment on crustaceans, quoted in every zoological textbook, the functioning of the organs of static equilibrium. I could give further examples, but these investigations remained isolated and lacked system. The young discipline did not begin to thrive until Hans Winterstein, a medical physiologist like Exner, Bethe and Kreidl, published from 1911 to 1925 his *Handbuch der vergleichenden Physiologie* (Handbook of Comparative Physiology) in which the information scattered in the literature was collected and subordinated to a unifying approach. Later, comparative physiology paid her debt to human physiology with compound interest, for many physiological processes in human organs become much more intelligible when seen against this broad canvas.

Naturally I also suggested subjects for comparative physiology to some of the first students who came to write their theses under my supervision. My very first pupil, Anton Himmer, worked on a problem of colour changes, and the second, Ruth Beutler, who remained my faithful collaborator to the day of her death, studied the physiology of digestion in lower animals.

I myself fell once more irresistibly under the spell of the honey-bees. The starting point for my new investigation lay in certain observations I had made in connection with my colour-and-smell training. Once the food dish was empty and nothing further to be obtained from that source, the foraging bees would stay away, and only occasionally a scout would turn up to reconnoitre. But if one of these found the dish refilled and returned home with a full load, the whole company of foraging bees was buzzing round the dish again within a few minutes. It was clear to me that the bee community possessed an excellent intelligence service, but how it functioned I did not know. This gave me no rest.

In the spring of 1919 I sat and watched a small colony of bees in the picturesque garden courtyard of our Institute at the Old Academy (Fig. 17). The Inspector of Apiculture for Bavaria, a

F

man named Hofmann, had lent me a queen-breeding cage. This
had the advantage that the inmates were unable to hide themselves
from view, for it contained only a single honeycomb which could
be observed through glass from both sides. I attracted a few bees

FIG. 17. View from my window at the Munich Zoological
Institute of the garden courtyard where I experimented with
bees. In the background Munich's landmark, the Frauenkirche.
(*Photograph Dr. Ecke.*)

to a dish of sugar water, marked them with red paint and then
stopped feeding for a while. As soon as all was quiet, I filled the
dish up again and watched a scout which had drunk from it after
her return to the hive. I could scarcely believe my eyes. She performed a round dance on the honeycomb which greatly excited the

marked foragers around her and caused them to fly back to the feeding place. This, I believe, was the most far-reaching observation of my life. In the course of time it gave rise to some three dozen papers of my own and as many studies by my pupils. The resulting discoveries also led to many enjoyable lecture tours and gave me many opportunities of seeing foreign countries.

Of course, I did not at once foresee any of this. My immediate concern was with the construction of more suitable observation hives and the development of a better marking system for bees. After 3 years of intensive research I thought I knew the "language" of the bees. Reverting to the subject 20 years later, I realized that I had overlooked the most crucial point, and that four times as many years and a vastly greater team of collaborators were insufficient to exhaust the unsolved riddles of the bees' language.

If we experiment today to clear up individual aspects of the whole complex we frequently have twelve or more observers acting in concert. In the beginning, things were on a more modest scale.

In practical matters I relied on advice from Guido Bamberger, a highly competent bee-keeper. He was an excellent observer and his experience enabled him to make many useful suggestions. Quite often when I went to the Institute garden of a Sunday morning to enjoy the bliss of work without interruptions my wife would offer me her welcome help. This meant she had to walk all the way from Schwabing to town, pushing the perambulator in front of her. During the time we watched and worked, Hannerl was usually stowed away in an old horse-trough. Even then science did exact her due at the expense of family life—one cannot combine the two without making concessions.

As soon as term ended we went to Brunnwinkl, where the great diversity of topography and landscape made me embark on more varied experiments and where I had more willing helpers at my disposal. One of our first "long-distance" experiments, admittedly rather primitive, concerned the size of the area searched by bees alerted by a round dance. For we soon discovered that after an interval in feeding the dances did not only recall the original foragers but also brought many others which had not previously been to the site. When a bee returns from a visit to certain flowering plants and starts dancing the other bees learn from the smell adhering to her which specific scent they have to look for. But that a dancing bee should, moreover, be capable of imparting to the other members of the hive the exact location of a food source was something which at that time I should not have believed possible. I assumed that following persistent dancing the newcomers among the foragers would first search the immediate neighbourhood of the hive and gradually extend the area of their search until they came upon the desired goal by accident.

This was the assumption I decided to test. The part relating to the immediate surrounding of the hive had already been proved, but in the last experiment of the series I kept watch by a little dish of honey placed inconspicuously on the ground somewhere in the middle of a large meadow at a distance of 1 km from the hive across hills and forests. Some marked bees were fed near the hive. They danced as soon as they returned to it. The honey had been perfumed with a few drops of essential oil so as to give the same distinctive fragrance both to the nearby and the distant feeding place. It was important to find out whether any bees arriving at my distant food dish were from our observation hive, or possibly strangers from other, nearer hives that found it by accident. We therefore agreed that after I had marked a visitor with paint, I would signal its departure to my brother Hans, who was posted on a hill top halfway between my observation post and the hive, by a blast on an old cow horn, a primitive instrument much treasured by our colony. He would then have the job of alerting a further helper by ringing a cow-bell, and that third man would pass on the message by means of a trumpet signal to the observers at Brunnwinkl, who would then watch with redoubled attention for the return of the labelled forager.

My poor brother had brought his pipe along, but had left his tobacco pouch behind—which made his vigil something of an ordeal, for the experiment turned out to be a test of patience and perseverance. After 4 hours, during which my little dish remained deserted, I was about to give up. But just then a foraging bee approached, obviously searching; she alighted on the dish and regaled herself on the honey: I marked her before she flew off again. Never before or since have I blown into a cow horn with such fervour! Everything worked. The bee really came from our hive and I was tremendously pleased with the positive result. We now know that this particular bee was an exception, an outsider, of a type whose unconventional behaviour sometimes benefits the community, and that dozens of bees would have found the isolated food dish even at that distance if they had been told of its whereabouts in their bees' language. But since the dancing bees had found their food source 16 yards away from the hive, they had absolutely no reason to send their fellow foragers farther afield.

Later we extended experiments of this nature and other tests over distances of 5–10 km cross-country. We learned to employ field telephones and other modern technological aids. But the main features never changed: all observers had to remain alert for hours on end even if nothing happened. Not everyone is capable of such concentration, and the choice of the right collaborators is therefore of the greatest importance. Only the experimenter-in-chief is proof against boredom and in a constant state of tense expectation, for to him, every experiment is a new exciting experience that will either confirm his hypotheses or confront him instead with new problems and unexpected riddles.

AS PROFESSOR IN ROSTOCK, 1921–1923

IN THE late autumn of 1921 I was appointed Professor of Zoology and Director of the Zoological Institute of Rostock University. It was characteristic of those times that I first learned about this impending event through a letter which reached me in September from a complete stranger, the then Professor of Physics at Rostock. He wrote:

Confidential

Dear Dr. von Frisch,   *Rostock, 23 September 1921*

Since you have every prospect of becoming Becher's successor at this University—the faculty having placed your name first on the list —I am writing to inquire whether in that case we might not arrange an exchange of living accommodation? I am, at my own request, retiring as from 1 October, and wish to take up residence in or near Munich, provided I can get a residence permit. This would of course be easiest to obtain by means of such an exchange. I would add that if you do not like my abode, you could always exchange it against something more suitable (bigger or smaller, as the case may be) but that otherwise you may have to wait years before you find what you need. . . .

Yours, etc.

A. HEYDWEILLER

The official confirmation, in the form of a telegram from the Minister of Education in Schwerin, did not come until late in the evening on 12 October. Overjoyed, I went at once to tell Hertwig who, seeing my beaming face, exclaimed from the doorstep, "Well, my boy, so you did get the job!" He had been absolutely certain all along. I myself never believed in an appointment until I had the official confirmation in my pocket.

A letter of congratulation from Hans Spemann added to our pleasurable expectations. Spemann, then Professor of Zoology at Freiburg, had been Becher's predecessor at Rostock, and therefore in a manner of speaking my grandfather in my new post. From the very beginning I had been fascinated by his work, and I derived the keenest pleasure from his papers because of the logic of his experiments, the cautious formulation of his conclusions, and the beauty of his style. We later became close friends. At that time he wrote:

Dear von Frisch,   *Freiburg, 15 October 1921*

I am so very pleased to hear that you got the Rostock chair. . . . Rostock is the only place for which I occasionally feel something like homesickness. True, the first impression from the station is anything but prepossessing, but I know you will come to love the old city and its beautiful surroundings, its churches, towers and squares more and more as time goes on. When I think of my room at the Institute looking out on the old trees in Blücher Square and onto the tower of St. Jacobus', perennially circled by gulls, those graceful messengers from a nearby sea, I could envy you. Give my love to the dear old Institute . . . and think kindly of your predecessor who had it completely rebuilt . . . (*and* had the settee in your room re-covered in flowery chintz!). But chiefly I want you to remember me to the old members of the staff, to Falkenberg, Geinitz, and Geffken.

With all good wishes,
Yours,
H. SPEMANN

We really did have a most pleasant time there. After 35 years spent as ordinary Professor and head of university institutes in four different cities I can say with conviction that we were never happier than during our brief stay at Rostock.

Because this was my first professorial appointment, my predecessor Becher made a point of handing over the Institute with great thoroughness and of introducing me fully into the local atmosphere. For an institute is like a living organism. Its well-being and functioning depend very largely on its head. A change at the top amounts to a crisis viewed with apprehension by staff and students alike. When everything had been discussed in great detail, Becher concluded by way of encouragement: "Of course you realize that as professor and head of the Institute you are something like a king in your little domain."

I often thought of this remark: not only while it was still true that the Professor, backed by the confidence of the authorities, was entirely his own master, but even more so when under National Socialism both confidence and ancient liberties were gradually lost —and often enough the job too, unless one was prepared to howl with the wolves.

Rostock had a reputation of being an excellent springboard for an academic career. Because the small state of Mecklenburg could not afford to pay its professors well, the authorities were on the look-out for young talent that could be had cheaply. As, naturally, some of them were duds, and many of the good ones they picked were snapped up by some better-endowed university before long, there was a constant supply of new young blood. In this way what was called the "University of beginners" was more stimulating than many a more famous seat of learning.

In the Zoological Institute I found a book in which each director had left an account of his activities and a portrait of himself. Perusing this neat little volume my wife and I worked out that the average tenure of office of zoologists had been 7 years. We therefore prepared ourselves mentally for a similar duration of stay.

The exchange of living accommodation worked eventually, though not without some effort. Heydweiller's elegant house was too expensive for us, while our flat in Munich was not quite what he wanted either. Both he and we had to find new partners for further exchanges, and in the end the barter involved five people. We ourselves found at 101 Friedrich-Franz Strasse a pleasant, spacious flat, with a garden attached, situated in a decent neigh-bourhood. Its occupant, an ex-naval officer, was most willing to move into Heydweiller's much better appointed house, but being an honest man, he felt he had first to point out to me a serious drawback of his place. He took me down to the cellars, and con-fessed with serious, almost tragic mien that huge black slugs had from time to time been sighted there. He was greatly relieved, though rather incredulous, when he found that this did not deter a zoologist.

Then came the great day of "general post" when five furniture vans started rolling on one and the same day. When not many days later our pantechnicon stood in the Friedrich-Franz Strasse, I was called home urgently from the Institute to find my wife almost in tears helplessly facing a group of local removal men. For though her native tongue as well as theirs was German, neither side could understand a word of what the other said. I myself fared little better, despite my love for the works of Fritz Reuter, a famous writer of delightful books in the Mecklenburg Low German patois. However, with some good will and much gesticulating every piece of furniture was eventually put where we wanted it. And when later we discovered that a swarm of wild bees had settled in a hole in our garden wall we took it as an omen that providence was blessing our new abode.

Thinking back on our Rostock days I believe that three factors contributed to our happiness there.

First, I had achieved the position which is the ambition of every "private lecturer", but needs a good deal of luck on top of other qualifications. I was thoroughly enjoying my new job and plunged with zest into my work at the small yet pleasant institute.

Second, town and countryside offered much that was new to us. The old town with its charming churches and towers was quite small, and all other parts where one might have business were also within easy walking distance. Yet the nearness of the harbour of Warnemünde and of the fashionable Baltic resorts brought a more cosmopolitan flavour. There were modern shops, a good theatre, and excellent concerts. It was beautiful on the banks of the Warnow, the broad navigable river that linked the town to the coast of Warnemünde about 10 km away, especially when the wide evening sky would blaze in flaming colours. I loved the sandy dunes along the Baltic, and the coastal forests on Rostock Heath with their gnarled, windswept pines. But the sea itself I found disappointing. Compared to what the Adriatic had had to offer, animal life in the almost brackish waters of the Baltic was indescribably poor. And in place of the many steamers, large or small, bound for all the four corners of the world, the only representative of modern shipping appeared to be the ferry boat to Denmark, and even that did not go very often. It really was a bit of quite exceptionally bad luck for the film company which happened to shoot the story of Columbus on the coast of Warnemünde at the time when the smoking funnels of that ferry boat appeared on the film behind the gorgeous medieval galleons reconstructed at great expense.

However, I do not want to be unjust. As a zoologist I was amply compensated for the dearth of interesting marine life in the Baltic by the richness of the avian fauna. We got to know the region's bird life in many interesting excursions which took us to the wistful, melancholy landscape of the Müritz or to the nearby island of Langenwerder where thousands of gulls and other seabirds nested in a restricted space. This bird island was something of a worry to us. Times were hard, food was scarce, and gulls' eggs much in demand. The breeding sites were being robbed of their eggs, and naturalists feared for the continuing existence of this bird paradise. A government commission was asked to inspect it and to arrange legal protection for the birds. A colleague of mine had organized the tour most efficiently, but he had forgotten to warn the members of the commission against wearing their best clothes. When the birds, disturbed by our intrusion, rose into the air like a white cloud and proceeded to defend their breeding place in the customary manner by a bombardment from their rear hatches, the result was not entirely beneficial to the black coats worn by some of the gentlemen from the Ministry.

In our first year at Rostock the sea showed itself from an unexpected side. Though the local climate was supposed to be mild, the frost in the winter of 1921–2 was so severe and prolonged that the Baltic was frozen as far as the eye could see. For us the ice piled high near the beach and the vast motionless expanse beyond was just a beautiful and exciting spectacle. But for the local people for whom the sea encompassed life and death, it was far more. "The sea in fetters" moved them to the core.

Last but not least it was the people, both of the university and outside it, which made life in Rostock so pleasant for us. There was somehow an atmosphere of friendly fellowship, and much more social intercourse than at larger places. It was customary for each newly appointed member of the university to hire a cab one Sunday morning and to leave cards at the houses of his colleagues. The following Sunday they would then all pay their return visits and inspect the newcomers. My wife and I, both little used to society, found that day somewhat overpowering. My wife maintains to this day that I either did not introduce the callers to her at all or introduced them under a wrong name. Even on this very first occasion, however, we made some pleasant contacts from which a lifelong friendship developed with the anatomist C. Elze and the physiologist H. Winterstein. With these and some others I founded a small scientific circle in which each of us in turn would read an essay of reasonably general interest from his own special field. We always met at the home of that particular evening's lecturer, whose wife was expected to minister to our bodily wants but to disappear later, leaving the field to science. It was characteristic of the good atmosphere at this university that another much larger group also met regularly to learn from lectures of a general nature what were the chief problems agitating the minds in the various disciplines.

Dr. Hermann Pflüger, an ophthalmic surgeon, and his vivacious wife became our closest friends. Their two little boys were of the same age as our brace of little girls, and often one mother would look after all four little ones to allow the other some rest. But it was music that brought us together in the first place, for Dr. Pflüger was a violinist and became the first fiddle of our quartet. We all lived within a stone's throw of each other and if one of us felt like playing after supper, he needed only go round and whistle under the other fellows' windows—true, he could not call them any other way, for house doors were bolted at dusk in this little provincial town and there were few door bells—much less telephones.

One such evening we sat and played until late, though my wife was due to leave for Vienna the next morning. At last we said goodbye to our guests and my wife started packing. Suddenly the whole gang reappeared outside our windows, having climbed the scaffolding which happened to be up, and clamoured for more cakes and wine. What could we do but let them in again?

Though Dr. Pflüger played well, we (including himself) felt a desire for an even higher standard of music making. We therefore occasionally invited the leader of the local opera orchestra to play the first violin. These evenings were especially delightful. Friends who came to listen turned the evenings into pleasant social functions. Later, we ourselves and other university people invited the leader and other members of the orchestra to our homes for highly enjoyable concerts before a larger circle of invited guests.

Before long, however, our musicians were forbidden by their employers to accept private engagements for fear of competition— an instance of characteristic small-town pettiness. Yet the smallness of the town had its compensations. When we henceforth listened to their playing at the concert hall or the opera house, we could always slip home in the interval to make sure that everything was all right.

Despite the long journey we did, of course, go to Brunnwinkl for the summer. The first glorious days in the mountains after 10 months in a country as flat as the proverbial pancake brought me a curious psychological experience—the hills and slopes surrounding our little valley appeared to be far steeper and higher than I remembered them, their visual impression contrasting strongly and compulsively with their mental image.

At Brunnwinkl I worked once more on bees. But at Rostock I turned to a new problem concerning the senses of fish. The question whether or not fish can hear had been hotly debated for some time. They possess neither ear lobes, nor auditory canals, nor a middle ear. Moreover, their inner ear contains no cochlea, which in man is thought to be the seat of hearing. The labyrinth of the vertebrates is a highly complex structure serving both the sense of hearing and that of equilibrium. According to Helmholtz's theory of resonance and its more recent modifications, only one section of the labyrinth is concerned with the perception of sound: in humans and other mammals this section is the cochlea; it is shaped like a helix and contains the delicate basilar membrane. A corresponding structure, though shaped somewhat differently, is found in all terrestrial vertebrates, but nothing resembling it exists in the labyrinth of fish (Fig. 18). By its structure the inner ear of fish appeared to be exclusively an organ of balance. Most anatomists, physiologists, and ear specialists were therefore convinced that fish must be deaf. Yet not all zoologists and physicists did share this view.

The question was one of fundamental importance. If it were shown that fish possessed a genuine auditory sense, i.e. a capacity for perceiving and analysing sound through their inner ear, this would mean that neither cochlea nor basilar membrane was indispensable for hearing. The fact that a principle was involved explains the heat engendered by this controversy. Reliable observers maintained they had repeatedly seen flight movements and other reactions following the sounding of whistles, bells, etc. Catfish were frequently mentioned in this connection. Members of the other camp stated that they had tried in vain to make such observations. One of the chief protagonists of the deafness theory, O. Körner, also used catfish as test animals. He whistled to them in many different ways, with his mouth, through his fingers, on penny

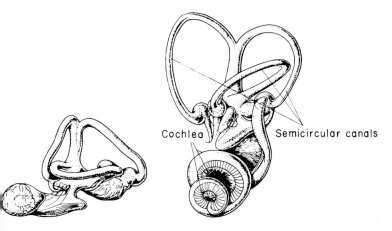

Cochlea   Semicircular canals

FIG. 18. *To the left:* the labyrinth of a minnow; *to the right:* a human labyrinth. The utriculus with the semicircular canals serves as a balancing organ.

whistles, high or low, but in vain. He even asked a famous singer to sing to them, but the fish were no more moved by her trills and shakes than by his own common or garden whistling. They did not give the slightest sign of sound perception.

O. Körner was a Professor of Otology at Rostock University and director of the ear clinic there. I cannot tell today whether this circumstance had something to do with my desire to investigate the hearing of fish; in any case I acquired a catfish. I then argued as follows: if I were a small fish, I should be interested in earthworms and other delicacies of the kind, but hardly in the coloratura of a famous soprano which normally would not be in the least relevant to my survival. However, a fish might perhaps be induced to take an interest in music with the help of food training techniques such as had already proved so useful to me in clarifying similar problems.

If the fish was to be taught to respond to sound, it would clearly be best if he could not see at all what was happening around him. A catfish has minute eyes which mean very little to him. They can easily be removed without affecting his normal way of life and this was done. In order to make the aquarium comfortable for the little blind fellow, I got hold of an old hollow earthenware candlestick and knocked off its base so that it formed an open-ended tube. The fish—we called him Xaverl—at once chose it as his quarters. Several times a day I approached the aquarium and whistled a few notes immediately before offering some bits of meat on a stick to the wide mouth which showed at one end of the tube. These were snapped up greedily. On the sixth day of training I saw to my delight that Xaverl made a movement forward immediately after my whistling performance, even before I had dipped the stick with the food into the water. In thirty subsequent repeats Xaverl invariably came out when I whistled, be it ever so softly.

I invited Professor Körner to come and look at my experiments. Unlike C. von Hess (cf. p. 49), he accepted with alacrity. While the kindly old gentleman sat in front of the aquarium waiting for the experiment he was convinced could not succeed, I went to the farthest corner of the room and gave a soft whistle. Xaverl at once came out of his tube, and at the same time the Professor, almost visibly deflated, could be heard to say reluctantly: "There is no doubt. The fish comes when you whistle."

I have told this story at some length because it became the starting point for a series of experiments on the hearing capacity of fish which later, in Munich, was to occupy myself and my pupils for many years. I shall describe very briefly what they were about.

Building on my results with Xaverl, my pupil H. Stetter was able to elucidate the range and quality of hearing in catfishes and minnows by carefully executed food conditioning experiments. Their perception of very soft sounds differed little from that of human ears. Even more surprising was the fact that despite the different structure of their inner ear they could distinguish pitch quite well, as was shown by a method of positive and negative conditioning. A fish is first trained to expect food when he hears a whistle of a given pitch. As soon as it has grasped this and shows reliable responses, we sound another note, say, a lower one, to which, naturally enough, the fish responds in the same manner. Now, however, it receives a slight slap with a glass rod instead of the expected titbit. If it has experienced a reward with one note and a punishment with another sufficiently often, it will respond to the first by a search for food, and to the second by inactivity or even flight, demonstrating thereby that it is capable of distinguishing the sounds. Later experiments with improved techniques showed that fish can distinguish between semitones and even quartertones in the medium wavelengths.

In view of these results the hearing capacity of fish could hardly be doubted. Yet they did not amount to strict proof, as they might also be attributable to very sensitive tactile sensations of the epidermis. For sound waves are, after all, vibrations of the surrounding medium, be it air or water, and we ourselves are capable of feeling them provided they are strong enough. To be able to speak with absolute conviction of a sense of hearing in fish comparable to our own, it was necessary to prove that their reaction to sound was mediated by their labyrinth.

The labyrinth of fish is not easily accessible to operative manipulations. Yet with some ingenuity and the help of suitable instruments, we succeeded in removing any desired part of the inner ear without upsetting the functioning of the remaining parts and without affecting the animal's normal behaviour and appetite. Incidentally, my practical experience in surgery, gained during the war, was very useful to me. In this way we were able to establish that a certain part of the labyrinth serves the sense of balance, while another part—which in land animals has become the cochlea— that of hearing. Neither cochlea nor basilar membrane is therefore indispensable for sound perception and differentiation, though they may improve the quality of hearing.

When we tested the hearing capacity of different species we found that some could hear very well and others much less so. Those with a well-developed auditory sense include the large family

of cyprinids to which most of our freshwater fish belong, and the
silurids. These all possess a remarkable anatomical peculiarity. A
series of small bones or ossicles forming an articulated chain links
their swim-bladder, which is filled with gas and is very taut, to the
inner ear through a hole in the rear part of the cranium. When
sound waves cause the elastic membrane of the bladder to vibrate,
these vibrations are transmitted to the organ of hearing exactly like
those of a vibrating eardrum are fed to the inner ear by the small
bones of the middle ear. In both cases the auxiliary mechanism

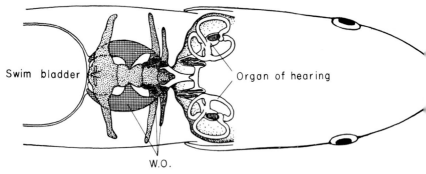

Swim bladder   Organ of hearing

W.O.

FIG. 19a

Fig. 19a, b. Mechanisms for intensifying acuity of hearing in
fish and man—a remarkable parallel. Fig. 19a: Front part of
minnow. Vibrations caused by sound waves in the swim-bladder
are transferred by the Weberian ossicles (W.O.) and a canal system
to the organ of hearing.

greatly enhances the acuity of hearing (Fig. 19a, b). What is so
remarkable is the fact that the same effect is being achieved in an
entirely different way. For anatomically there is no relationship
between our bones of the middle ear (hammer, anvil, and stirrup)
and the Weberian ossicles which perform a similar function in
fish. The technical expression for such a phenomenon is "convergence". It is just one of many instances of nature's "inventiveness". There are others in the same field.

All species possessing Weberian ossicles have good hearing but
not all fish without them have necessarily poor hearing. We dis-

covered other families whose hearing was acute, for instance the mormyrids, a strange type of African fish at home in muddy waters where eyes are not of much use. They possess no Weber's organ, but already during embyonal development their swim-bladder forms two symmetrical sac-like appendages, the ends of which develop into small, taut, gas-filled, bubble-shaped structures. These adhere tightly to an opening of the skull close to the labyrinth in such a way that the vibrations of their elastic membranes are

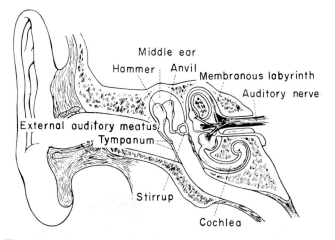

Fig. 19b: Human ear. The vibrations of the eardrum are trans-ferred to the organ of hearing by the three auditory ossicles of the middle ear (hammer, anvil, and stirrup).

transmitted directly to the ear. Other families show yet other arrangements. It is almost as if nature had experimented with the lower vertebrates in order to discover how best to bring the newly "invented" labyrinth in contact with the sound waves from the outer world.

Here the reader will probably wonder what benefit a fish may derive from a sense of hearing. It is not generally known that many fish produce sounds and noises which help members of a species to find each other. Moreover, feeding, predators, the impact of waves on the shore, etc., may give rise to a variety of sounds which mean

G

something to fish though they are concealed from the tourist who contemplates the stillness of a sheet of water.

These things do, however, belong to a later era, and I want briefly to return to our Rostock period so as not to leave out completely one of the harsher aspects of life at that time. I refer to the galloping German inflation. The value of money fell literally from day to day. Prices soared by leaps and bounds. Salaries were paid in instalments every other day and any money that was not at once exchanged bought only a fraction of the same things the next day. On pay days Hannerl, our eldest, then 4 years old, regularly came to collect from me at the Institute the millions of marks designed to feed the family for the next couple of days. As we happened to hear from friends, she sometimes boasted to strangers that she was carrying "lots of money" from her daddy to her mummy. Fortunately, this was in honest Rostock, and she was never robbed. It would hardly have been worth while, either. It goes without saying that our salaries did not keep step with the cost of living, and there were times when what we earned in a day would buy no more than a small packet of margarine. Feeding a large family became an almost insoluble problem. I remember how I once went with my wife to a dealer of second-hand clothes trying to raise some money on an old pair of shoes. The dealer looked at the well-worn pair and did not seem at all keen. But when he realized that a university professor was compelled to hawk his old boots around he was so horrified that he paid us a good price. I hope he had his reward.

The inflation still raged when we went to Breslau, which we did, not after the anticipated seven biblical years, but after a mere two, in the year 1923. I remember how on one occasion my wife's shopping basket was filled to overflowing with billions of marks in enormous bundles, the equivalent of a few paltry schillings my sister-in-law had sent us from Austria which by then was over the worst. In high spirits, we set out at once to convert our treasure into eatables before the shops closed. But alas it was Saturday. Nobody would sell us a scrap of food for money that could not be turned into merchandise before the week end. There we stood, clutching our basket full of paper, knowing that by Monday its purchasing power would be practically nil.

No one who has not experienced this wretched state of affairs can gauge the relief we felt when in November 1923 the currency was at last stabilized by the introduction of the Rentenmark. At first we got only part of our salary in this new, stable, currency. With something akin to reverence—tinged, admittedly, with slight doubts—I contemplated the first bank notes that were supposed to keep their value—and did. The whole thing was like a miracle, at any rate to someone like myself to whom financial matters will always be unfathomable mysteries. But we must retrace our steps to the summer of 1923.

BRESLAU, 1923–1925

ON THE 14th June 1923 my wife gave birth to her third baby at the Rudolfinerhaus in Vienna: "Another girl!" the nurse reported with some indignation. As my Breslau appointment was confirmed soon after we had all gone to Brunnwinkl, my wife and family never returned to Rostock and I arranged the move on my own. Afterwards I met my wife in Vienna to take her to Breslau. While I was registering our luggage, a typical Viennese standing behind me exclaimed aloud: "To Breslau! What on earth can induce a man to go to that hole!" This arrogant remark, which contrasted so strongly with Spemann's letter about Rostock, sent a slight shiver down my spine. But without reason.

Breslau turned out to be a large but beautiful city, with picturesque old quarters. The River Oder, with its many arms and islets, made it especially attractive, and in the manner of the local people traces of their Austrian past could still be discerned. So we soon felt at home, particularly as we were fortunate enough to find a beautiful, roomy flat at the outskirts of the city where our growing family could thrive and spread themselves.

The children provided me with excellent opportunities for comparative biological observations. It was amazing how different they were in behaviour and interests despite their common heredity. Hannerl was order personified and already a little housewife when quite small, a miniature version of what the mother of our three grandchildren is today. Often she would cry with rage when little Maria, who had lots of temperament but little discipline, caused hopeless chaos in their nursery possessions. One day when a flock of rooks flew cawing past the house, Maria—she must have been about 3 at the time—exclaimed excitedly: "Can you hear the sweet little swallows, daddy?" Another time, when she watched a butterfly settling on a flower, its wings aquiver, she was heard to say: "Oh look at the dear little quack quack froggie!" From that moment I felt sure that she was not likely to follow in my footsteps. But in Leni, the youngest, who is now my most valued assistant, a gift for observation and scientific concentration showed itself at an early age.

The Zoological Institute at Breslau was larger than that at Rostock, and with its vast main laboratory and lofty ceilings it seemed chilly and much less homely. But it possessed excellent equipment, a large library, and the necessary garden space. The impressive museum attached to it may have induced my predecessor, Franz Doflein (my friend from Munich days), to go to Breslau from Freiburg in 1918, for he was much interested in museum work. Alas, a terrible disease made him resign his post in 1923, and caused his untimely death in August 1924.

With the larger institute I was taking over there went, of course, a larger staff and an increased number of students writing their theses under me. This gave me the chance of widening the scope of my scientific work.

For scientific problems behave very much like that monster of fable, the nine-headed hydra, which grew two new heads for every head cut off. Every problem solved gives rise to two or three new ones, and soon the work involved exceeds the capacity of one man. In such circumstances we turn for help to our students who, tackling this or that individual aspect in their theses, become closely associated with our efforts. I do not believe there is anything that unites people more intimately than the joint pursuit of problems of common interest. And if the people working together in an institute happen also to like and respect each other as persons, then such a place becomes in truth a happy community, binding its members with strong invisible ties that withstand separation and the vicissitudes of fortune. These bonds may occasionally disappear from sight, yet they will assert themselves at once at chance meetings after lectures in remote cities, or on study tours in foreign lands, or at other times give rise to unexpected letters. These friendships are among the most beautiful and highly prized fruits of our work.

A small faithful band had followed me to Breslau. Among them Ruth Beutler, who had begun her doctoral thesis in Munich, and two of my students from Rostock, G. A. Rösch and W.

Wunder (Fig. 20), studying respectively the division of labour among the bees and the retina of fish.

This was a subject on which I had done some preliminary experiments at Rostock, and which fascinated me at the time: the duplicity theory of vision. The retina of all vertebrates contains

FIG. 20.   The staff at the Breslau Zoological Institute, taken in the Institute garden on 24 June 1924. *1st row, left to right:* Loebel, E. Matthes, K. v. Frisch, H. Giersberg, Ruth Beutler. *2nd row:* Kaethe Heyde (later Mrs. Giersberg), Miss Berger (later Mrs. Rösch, later Mrs. Heinroth), O. Harnisch, W. Wunder. *Last row:* Deichsel (stoker), Mentzes, Miss Küntzel, Rolle, F. Pax, Senf (museum assistant), Eva Gumpert, Mandowsky, Gassmann, G. A. Rösch, Müller (caretaker), Stober.

two kinds of sensory cells—the slender rods and the plumper cones. The duplicity theory assumes that the duality of shapes corresponds to a duality of function, the cones being concerned with colour vision and the rods colour blind. The cones cannot function in poor light. The rods can adapt themselves to decreasing illumination by increasing their sensitivity. In the dim light of the stars the cones hand over to the colour-blind rods, and we see all objects in shades of grey, whatever their daylight colour: all cats are grey in the dark.

This hypothesis was not undisputed. Nobody had actually seen the transition from cone vision to rod vision, because apparently this is entirely functional, the rods taking over the work of the cones without any visible change, so that it could only be inferred indirectly, at any rate in man and the higher vertebrates. However, it had been noticed that if fish were kept in bright light, the cones alone were in the front part of the retina, while the rods were buried in the pigment behind, but that if they had been kept in complete darkness for a time, the cones receded and the rods moved forward in the interstices between them into the plane of vision of the retina, performing a kind of minuet on a microscopic scale. This seemed to demonstrate *ad oculos* the changing of the guards between the two battalions of sensory cells. Yet the evidence was still not absolutely conclusive. For when it is perfectly dark it is no more possible to see with the rods than with the cones. Nothing was known about the position of the sensory cells and the vision of fish in dim light.

I therefore placed the aquaria with my experimental specimens in a room in which the light could be dimmed to any desired degree. My fish were first trained in bright light to search for food in a coloured dish. This they learned quickly enough, and thereafter were able to pick out the coloured dish from any number of dishes in various shades of grey even if the light was rather poor. But from a certain stage of semi-darkness—which coincided approximately with the degree of poor illumination which makes the colours disappear for us—the fish confounded the coloured dish with the grey ones, searching them all for food. This proved that they, too, became colour blind in semi-darkness. Histological examination confirmed that at this very point the cones receded and the rods took their place (Fig. 21a, b, c). Thus comparative physiology had provided strong additional evidence for the validity of the duplicity theory.

Although an increasing number of papers on comparative physiology were coming from various institutes, they were scattered over a great many zoological or physiological periodicals for lack of a specialized medium of publication. At my request the publisher Dr. Ferdinand Springer started a journal of comparative physiology, the *Zeitschrift für vergleichende Physiologie*. It appeared for the first time at Easter 1924, and is now (1966) in its 51st volume.

Long though the journey was from Breslau, it did not deter us from going to Brunnwinkl for the summer. From there I went to Innsbruck in September 1924 to attend the 88th meeting of the German Society for Natural Science and Medicine where I presented a report on my three years' study of the "language" of the

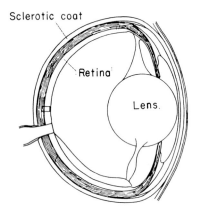

Fig. 21a. The eye of a fish.

bees. The success of this lecture was in no small measure due to the fact that it was intelligible acoustically. The naturalists' conference was developing into a mammoth affair of several thousand participants. The plenary sessions took place in a vast exhibition hall, which (of course) lacked the loudspeaker systems we now take for granted. When soon after I started I was asked from the back of the hall "to speak up" I fortunately adopted the right course: I spoke very slowly, and with meticulous articulation. In this way I managed to overcome a difficulty which was to defeat some of the other speakers.

The climax of my lecture was a film of the dancing bees—a

form of demonstration which at that time was still something of a novelty in scientific lectures. The dance of the bees is a fascinating spectacle, but one that can never be conveyed by words alone. To enable my audiences to see these exciting phenomena with their own eyes, I had filmed them, helped by an able cinema technician.

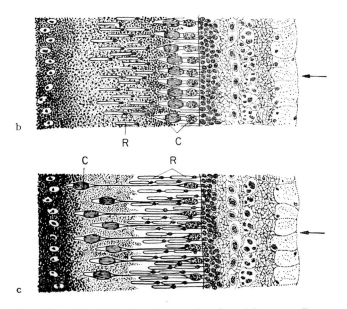

FIG. 21b, c. Detail of the retina greatly enlarged (corresponding to the rectangle on Fig. 21a): (b) in bright light, (c) in dim light or darkness. *C* the colour-sensitive cones; *R* the rods which are insensitive to colour but highly sensitive to light.

This technique proved its usefulness in many fields of biological teaching, and I soon possessed a sizable collection of films I had made myself or acquired from others. Under National Socialism all university teachers had to hand in any films they made to a Central State Board for Teaching Films, so as to make them available to the whole community. This was no doubt an admirable institution, but I confess that I found the confiscation, without so much as by your leave, of one's lawful spiritual property somewhat disconcerting.

Today there is some danger that films might be used to excess in academic teaching. Quite short sequences often suffice to make an audience visualize a train of events, particularly if shown during the lecture itself, not afterwards. A film projector should therefore be "a must" for biological lecture rooms.

At these jamborees of the Society for the Natural Sciences there were such crowds that you could hardly hope to find the people you wanted to meet, and so many things going on at the same time that you always missed the lecture you had particularly planned to hear. The meetings of the German Zoological Society were of a much more intimate character. True, I did not very often attend, because I have always avoided crowds rather than sought them. Yet these meetings have taken me to many a German university town I should otherwise never have seen. One of these was Königsberg, where the zoologists held their Whitsun conference of 1924. The proceedings inform me that 32 papers were read and 171 delegates (members and guests) took part. A gathering of this magnitude is still manageable and conducive to a fruitful exchange of ideas. Those who wanted an assistant or a likely successor would look around among the junior members, who, knowing this, were trying to excel in lectures and demonstrations. There was about these occasions a distinct flavour of a hiring fair.

On that occasion at Königsberg, the programme included an excursion to Rossitten which would have deserved to be enshrined in the annals of marine history. Rossitten is a little village on the Kurische Nehrung—a narrow sandy peninsula separating the small bay of Courland from the Baltic. When it still belonged to Germany it was the seat of a famous ornithological station, its position offering unrivalled opportunities for observing and studying the grandiose spectacle of bird migration. Its Director, J. Thienemann, had invited the conference to visit the station. We therefore boarded a little steamer at Labiau on the mainland which was to take us across the bay (Fig. 22). The low coast of the narrow peninsula, which was over 30 km away, could not be seen. When we had been steaming ahead for several hours under a cloudless sky, and ought by rights to have been there, the captain suddenly turned to some of us who were watching gulls from the bridge through our binoculars with the astonishing remark: "You gentlemen have field glasses. Could you tell me whether this is a wood to our right?" "Most certainly," we said, "but surely no glass is needed to see that?" Whereupon the captain: "In that case I have absolutely no idea where we are!" It turned out that we were actually heading for Kranz at the base of the peninsula. We had to

Fig. 22. The excursion to Rossitten, zoologists' Whitsun meeting, 1924. --------- intended course. ————— actual course.

execute a 180° turn and arrived at Rossitten many hours late, so that the programme planned for the day had to be cut severely. The captain's explanation was simple and incontrovertible. The vessel that had been chartered was a river steamer. As it was never in danger of losing its way, there was no compass on board.

Our stay at Breslau was short, no more than three terms, in fact. Though there was at that time no official retiring age for professors in Bavaria, Richard Hertwig, always critical, even towards himself, decided on reaching the age of 74 that it was time for him to go. When Spemann, his intended successor, preferred to stay at the smaller University of Freiburg, the chair was offered to me. I received the news of my appointment, which was for 1 April 1925, on 9 December 1924, the eightieth birthday of my mother. The wheel had come full circle. I returned to Munich to take charge of the department whence I had started out on my zoological pilgrimage.

BACK IN MUNICH

GREAT joy and deep sorrow so often, alas, come together. On 6 April 1925, when we were busily settling in again at Munich, death took away my mother. She had only taken to her bed a few days before she died, and probably had hardly realized that she was ill. Providence had granted her wish for a gentle parting.

I remember saying to her once when I was a boy how lucky I felt to have such a wonderful and quite exceptional mother. She replied that all children thought like that about their mamas. But even today, looking back over so many years, I still think that she was unique.

Throughout her rich and varied life she possessed a rare faculty for enjoying all that was good and beautiful. And since she knew how to find and bring out the best in all things and all men, she enjoyed every day of her life. That she herself was aware of this faculty we can infer from a letter she wrote to Gottfried Keller (dated 25 November 1880):

> You need not remind me of the skull behind the mask for I consciously enjoy every single day that God gives me: many people take this gift as a matter of course and thus miss a great joy that costs nothing. . . .*

This strongly positive attitude to life was enhanced by a heightened sensibility for all that makes life valuable. Because she

---

* To put this passage in its context I quote from two earlier letters:

Marie Frisch to G. Keller on 2 November 1880:

> Enclosed a photo taken at a fancy dress ball this spring to show you that despite my crowded nursery I still enjoy gaiety and fun. . . .

To which Keller replied on 21 November 1880:

> . . . and I thank you very much for the dainty photograph showing you in fancy dress with that adorable little cap. Your profile is as finely cut as eight or God knows how many years ago, and you look, if possible, younger. . . . But what is the good? The death's head will come, before we know where we are. . . .

hated gossip and futile talk, yet was always ready for serious or light-hearted conversation on worthwhile matters, she had gathered around her a large circle of like-minded friends. "To make life as

FIG. 23. Marie von Frisch. (*Charcoal drawing by Ferdinand Schmutzer.*)

enjoyable as possible for oneself and others" was how she once defined the meaning of existence. She herself was a past master in that art. In this she was aided by a quite unusual gift of empathy and intuition which enabled her to come to people's help at the right time and in the right manner. Of course, this often required money as well as tact. "Money means nothing to me—provided I have enough", she once said.

Towards us boys she was sparing in praise and rebuke. She believed in leaving us alone as much as possible, and taught us chiefly by her example. Yet by a quiet word at the right time she skilfully implanted certain principles of conduct deeply in our consciousness. My abhorrence of lies, for instance, was so strong that I never succumbed to the temptations coming from friends less scrupulous than myself.

Even at the great age of 80 she remained the focal point of her many relations and a large circle of friends, a wise counsellor whose shrewd advice was sought after in difficult situations, loved and revered by all for the warmth of her humanity, and that essential goodness which was at the core of her whole being and made her, for us, the measure of all things.

My own personal sense of loss was made especially poignant by the fact that 5 days after her demise I was offered a professorship in my native Vienna. This meant a difficult decision for me.

I had been familiar with the atmosphere of Vienna University since my childhood days and was linked to it by countless personal ties as to a beloved relative. I knew by experience how warmly the students of Vienna could respond to a teacher they loved. Never before or since have I seen such expressions of enthusiasm, such transports of devotion as when the Professor of Anatomy, Zuckerkandl, resumed his lectures after a serious illness, or when Hans Horst Mayer, the pharmacologist, had declined a call to Germany. And, most important, Vienna was home, luring us with much that we held dear consciously and all those imponderables which cannot be put into words.

But one thing did not attract me at all—the Zoological Institute. Situated in the main building of the university, in rooms that were much too large and lofty, without garden space or adequate facilities for keeping and observing living animals, it was ill equipped for experimental research. This prospect of greatly inferior conditions of work was decisive. I regretfully declined.

True, the Munich Institute was also bursting at the seams and lacking in modern facilities. But the large leafy courtyards of the erstwhile monastery offered opportunities for field research, and I had managed to have an annexe built which housed some excellent aquaria. Prospects for the future were also better in Munich.

A few words about the past history of the Institute and the conditions there at the time may be useful for the understanding of what follows. I quote from my presidential address to the 32nd annual meeting of the Zoological Society held at Munich in 1928:

Those of you who entered the old building of the Wilhelminum* for the first time probably have wondered whether it could possibly be true that our science was housed within its crumbling walls, and I freely admit that we shall conduct you around with somewhat mixed feelings; for in the narrow confines of this building, ten institutes and collections jostle each other cheek by jowl, all trying to expand in accordance with their own laws of development, and all cramped to suffocation. But for us zoologists there is a gleam of hope of a new institute on the horizon and that keeps up our spirits.

In tracing the history of zoology in Munich as is the custom, I shall try to be brief so as not to encroach on the time available for the proper objects of our meetings.

I must start with a confession: there is no proper documentary evidence for a zoological institute at Munich University. If we were lawyers, we would be in serious doubts about our existence.

The point is that originally there was only a zoological collection, in accordance with the older, purely systematic and anatomical approach. Out of this collection the institute grew so gradually and unobtrusively, that no actual act of foundation can be ascertained.

There is yet another peculiarity which our institute shares with some others: it is administratively divided between the University and the Bavarian Academy of Science. Fortunately we are not bureaucratic or we would constantly be stumbling over that demarcation line which cuts right across our staff, our inventory, and our budget. The reason is again an historical one. When King Ludwig I transferred the University from Landshut to Munich a hundred years ago he felt that the existing zoological museum and other collections of the Academy should serve the teaching of students and he therefore put them in charge of the professor concerned. Administratively we have remained a chimaera to this day.

In the hundred years since 1827 only three men held the chair of zoology. The first was von Schubert, a natural philosopher. His name means little today.

---

* Another name for the "Old Academy" after its founder.

His successor von Siebold started his career as Professor of Comparative Anatomy and Physiology in the Faculty of Medicine. How enviable a period in which one mind could still encompass several disciplines! But even then it was perhaps no easy feat. The story goes that Liebig, then Inspector General of Scientific Collections, secretly complained to the Minister about Siebold's physiology lectures, saying the fellow had no idea of his subject. As a result Siebold to his intense surprise (he was not even consulted) was made Professor of Zoology in 1854. We have every reason to be satisfied with this course of events. For this office which he took over when nearly 50 admirably suited his inclination and natural gifts. He not only reorganized and enriched the collections; to him we owe, *inter alia*, the scientific evidence for parthenogenesis in lepidoptera, bees, and wasps. It must have been a risky business to walk in this courtyard at the time for there were wasps' nests in all the bushes, lovingly tended by von Siebold who treated the objects of his research as personal friends—as every right-minded zoologist should. Though he had one or two gifted pupils, there was not yet an institute in the present sense of the word.

When he died in 1885, the vacancy was filled by the appointment of Richard Hertwig, whom we have the great pleasure of seeing in our midst today in undiminished vigour. Soon after he had taken over, Theodor Boveri, his first pupil and his greatest, arrived in Munich desiring to work here full time. No provision existed then for any kind of postgraduate research, but you, Sir, without hesitation cleared one of your own tables and carried it, with Boveri's help, into the next room. That action, I believe, constitutes the foundation of the Institute. Soon pupils came from near and wide, and a quarter century later there were fifty working places for undergraduates and full-time research workers. We told you, Sir, what drew us here on the occasion of your farewell lecture. I need not repeat myself among people whose warm attachment to your person is undiminished and ever present. . . .

Even after his retirement Richard Hertwig visited the Institute regularly. He turned again to his early love, the radiolaria, and worked on plankton samples he had once collected near Teneriffe. He remained with us, to our joy, for another 11 years, an exemplary ex-chief, never interfering but always ready to help with the full weight of his experience whenever he was needed.

Though we were tightly packed at the old Institute, we did not feel cramped, for the rooms were pleasant and cosy, and proximity was made easy by a spirit of joint endeavour, by youth and good temper. Often the senior students, the assistants, and myself, "the

H

Prof.", went skiing together in the mountains, or spent a week-end in a mountain hut rented by my friend, the physicist Arnold Sommerfeld. A carnival party towards the end of winter term became a firm tradition.

But to return to the research work of those years: the Old Academy was really not bad at all for the experiments I was then most interested in. I refer to the acoustic training of fish already mentioned (cf. p. 84). Not only myself, but several of my students (H. Stetter in particular), had their music pupils—minnows or other species—whose hearing capacity was being tested, not infrequently after certain operations had been performed on them. Each case involved weeks if not months of feeding tests to the sound of whistles. In this situation the general atmosphere of happiness and high spirits which made people want to sing and whistle for sheer exuberance was a positive menace. For what should our poor fish make of such sounds since for them a whistle signal meant "the cookhouse door"? We had to put up notices everywhere, even in the cloak room, saying "No whistling, please. No singing." It was equally important that no fish trainee should hear what was played or whistled to another. And for this, the massive, sound-deadening walls of the old monastery were a godsend. Nevertheless, we never had enough room and had to distribute our aquaria over all sorts of neighbouring departments, which were all most co-operative in offering us hospitality. Many an earnest visitor to the collection of fossils must have been sorely puzzled on suddenly hearing a whistling concert from behind some venerable witness of aeons of the world's history. These were not the only experiments with fish. Löwenstein studied the sense of equilibrium in minnows, and S. Dijkgraaf their sixth sense, the lateral line system which by its fantastic sensitivity to the slightest movements of water allows a fish to "feel" things at a distance. E. Scharrer worked on the light responses of their frontal eye (cf. p. 44) and Trudel tried to find out how good they were in distinguishing tastes. These and other research projects used minnows as experimental animals, as I had done in my thesis. They have always been one of my favourite objects of research, honey-bees, of course, being the other.

The layman may wonder why a biologist is content to devote 50 years of his life to the study of bees and minnows without ever branching out into research on, say, elephants, or at any rate the lice of elephants or the fleas of moles. The answer to any such question must be that every single species of the animal kingdom challenges us with all, or nearly all, the mysteries of life. Working on minnows in winter and bees in summer I have not so far run out of problems to investigate. By deliberately restricting ourselves to very few carefully chosen experimental animals we end up by knowing our subjects very well indeed. Without this familiarity we should not be in a position to interpret their behaviour under experimental conditions—just as the family doctor of old was able to notice and diagnose the slightest ailments of his patients because he knew them so well.

As always, the summer and, in particular, the months spent in Brunnwinkl were devoted to the bees. In earlier years I had been studying their colour vision and their sense of smell and had tried in vain to discover in them a sense of hearing. Now I felt I simply had to do something about our abysmal ignorance as to their sense of taste. I therefore embarked on what must have been the most tedious piece of research I ever tackled.

When I had practically finished my first investigation except for a few final supplementary experiments, my teacher, Sigmund Exner, remarked that all scientific work gets boring in the end if it is done properly. He referred, of course, to the necessity of checking and rechecking to make sure that there has been no error. But this study of the sense of taste in honey-bees was boring from the start. As it is not possible to train bees to tastes, the only possible method was to watch whether they would accept any given substance offered to them. For ten long summers my main occupation was to ascertain whether the bees said "yes" or "no" to the various dishes put before them. The only excitement lay in the formulation of the questions, i.e. the devising of ways and means which would compel the bees to answer them.

Bees have a sweet tooth almost by profession, as the nectar of flowers is their chief food, in exchange for which they perform the service of pollination for their hosts.

Since sugar is of such paramount importance in the bees' household one would expect them to be especially responsive to sweetness. But the opposite is the case. Compared to ourselves, bees need ten times the amount of sugar in a given quantity of water to experience it as sweet. Actually, this has been very wisely arranged by Mother Nature. For if the foragers were satisfied with weak sugar solutions, the honey made therefrom would not keep— no more than jam does if the housewife has been stingy with the sugar.

Bees are as old as the hills. Millions of years before there were human beings on this planet they have been busy collecting the sugary secretions of flowers. This may be one of the reasons why they appear to be so mature, so perfect in many ways, and why their biological relationships are reflected even in the most elementary functions of their sense organs.

Another instance of this lies in the selectivity of their taste. There are many kinds of sugar apart from the cane-sugar we use in tea or coffee, for instance glucose (used by athletes as a rapid source of energy), fructose, maltose, and many others. All are closely related chemically and most of them taste sweet to our tongues. To bees, on the other hand, most of them have no taste, and only about half a dozen are experienced as sweet. These are precisely the kinds of sugar that occur in their natural food. The fact that the bees recognized as sweet no more than a small fraction of the nearly three dozen sugars on which they were tested made me hope that I might find out some facts about the relationship between chemical structure and the property of sweetness, which our human sense of taste could not provide. It was chiefly for this reason that I persevered with these experiments for so many years. As I myself lacked the detailed chemical knowledge required, I sought the advice of Richard Willstätter. The fact that this great chemist, who certainly knew as much if not more about the subject matter than anyone else, required notice of my questions before our sessions together impressed me greatly. I could not have wished for a more conscientious adviser.

Though the work produced some interesting results, its main object eluded us. We know the biological but not the physiological reason why some sugars taste sweet to bees and others do not.

Of course, the bees were not offered sugar only. They were tested on all sorts of nasty stuff as well. I do not know whether they minded very much. But I can still see the faces of my children when they were made to taste sugar solutions with a dash of quinine added and other horrid things of the kind. I needed comparisons with humans, and the family had, as usual, to act as guinea-pigs. But since they also had to taste some of the real sugar solutions, I suppose they were not treated too badly.

The results of these investigations are recorded in a paper of 156 pages which, I am sure, no one will read for pleasure.

Yet I much prefer to write so as to give pleasure to my readers. That was one of the reasons why I decided to write popular books. The first suggestion that I should do so came from Richard Goldschmidt, who asked me in 1927 whether I would write the first volume of a series he had planned under the title *Verständliche Wissenschaft* (Science You Can Understand). In the peace and quiet of Brunnwinkl, I wrote the slim little book *Aus dem Leben der Bienen* (The Life of the Bees) during the few short weeks of an Easter vacation.*

It is no less important to write lucidly and well in scientific papers than in popular articles or books. No doubt this is largely a matter of inborn aptitude, but not entirely. I do not think it is my imagination that my style improves if during periods of creative writing I choose for my bedside reading authors who express themselves exceptionally well.

I am sure one should never dictate, but write one's draft in longhand and later type out a fair copy oneself. For this is the best way to find and correct those occasional awkward passages which are bound to occur from time to time. However, I do not suppose there are any infallible rules applicable to everybody—more is the pity.

Lecturing is another activity where clarity of presentation is crucial for success. But I do not intend to talk about its problems at this juncture. I only want to mention a lecture which I did *not* give. Soon after I had taken over at Munich the director of the famous Circus Sarrasani came to see me. He asked whether he might lecture to the students as he wanted to tell them about his work as an animal trainer, which he exercised not merely for gain but out of interest in animal psychology and fondness for his charges. I suggested that he should take my place in the ugly old

---

* An English translation was published by Methuen, London, under the title *The Dancing Bees*.

lecture theatre holding 300 people at the last lecture of the summer term. He gave a charming account of his experiences to a crowded auditorium and tried to convince us that the teaching of tricks was not cruelty to animals. As evidence of the fact that some positively enjoy it, he told a story about an elephant which he was trying to teach the headstand. One day, when he entered the elephant's stable, he found his pupil secretly practising the new trick entirely on his own.

When the lecture was over the whole audience was invited to enter a fleet of coaches drawn up at the gate which took them to the evening performance of the circus as the director's guests. This climax certainly beat any demonstrations I myself had been giving during term into a cocked hat.

I have not mentioned yet where we lived this time. We found a nice flat at Giselastrasse 5, again in Schwabing. We soon discovered that contrary to Rostock or Breslau, Munich lies astride one of the busiest crossroads of Europe. Our first guest to stay the night arrived before we had even time to settle in, and all the time we were there we had plenty of nice visitors; almost too many, in fact, for a man who wants to get on with his work.

When, chiefly because of the children's health, we later moved to a garden suburb farther out, things became quieter. In the garden suburb of Alt-Harlaching we found a house, Über der Klause 10, which was exactly what we wanted. There was an orchard with fifty-nine fruit trees, and the former owner's coat of arms, which adorned the wrought-iron balcony railings, showed two fishes, probably because his family had been pastors for generations.* Remembering the bees in Rostock, we took this for a good omen, and we have never regretted our purchase.

Alt-Harlaching then was a little cluster of houses surrounded by fields and pastures which looked rather haughtily down its nose on the "upstart" new suburb of Neu-Harlaching. Not far from our house there was a timber landing, where the logs that came floating down the river in rafts were pulled ashore and reloaded on to horse-drawn carts with plenty of noise and bustle, and a little below it

---

* The Greek word for fish, *ichthys*, was used as a symbol by the early Christians because its letters formed the initials of the words *Iesous Christos, Theou Hyos, Soter*—Jesus Christ, the Son of God, our Saviour.

there was the "Marienklause" (St. Mary's Close), a beautiful old place of pilgrimage. In May, the month of the Virgin Mary, we could see the flickering torches of the pilgrims who came in long processions to the little church, especially during the Third Reich, when such devotional zeal was rather frowned upon from above. We stayed in this idyllic spot until the bombs turned our house into a heap of smoking rubble, and here we live again in a newly built, smaller home.

Although things had slowly improved, students and young research workers were very hard up compared with the time before the First World War. It was not often that one of them could afford to go abroad. In this situation, the International Education Board founded in 1923 by John D. Rockefeller was a real blessing. Its grants enabled young scientists to go abroad to widen their horizon and pursue their researches, if necessary, at far-off universities. It was a principle of the foundation to vet each application with great care, as the money should be spent where it would yield the greatest benefit—one might almost say, profit, for science.

One of the representatives who visited us in summer term 1926 to interview candidates for grants was Professor A. Trowbridge, a physicist. After he had learned what he wanted to know and we had had a pleasant chat in my rooms I saw him off the premises. It was the hour of the beginners' practical. As we had no lecture room available, this was held in a corridor, and the students sat in a long row along a passage constantly used by all visitors to the Institute and to the collections. Jokingly, I said to the Professor: "You see for yourself how we are placed. Couldn't you build us a new Institute?" To my surprise he replied quite seriously: "I think it might be feasible. Please write me a letter explaining the circumstances in detail." This was the beginning of negotiations which—albeit after 5 long years—led to the rebuilding of the Munich Zoological Institute.

There were innumerable delays. Because I thought that the Rockefeller Foundation was chiefly interested in medicine, my first letter stressed the importance of biological studies for the training of doctors. The result was a curt refusal, for the department to which I had addressed myself was not interested in medicine. I had to start afresh, describing this time the handicaps under which we laboured in our biological research. The chief difficulty, however, lay in the principles of the Foundation which made them unwilling to do more than make a contribution towards the building of a new zoological institute, while, on the other hand, the Bavarian authorities were unable to promise any sums towards such a project. In the end Professor Trowbridge met us halfway and declared that he would accept the provision of a building site and the promise of a detailed annual budget for staff and other expenses as sufficient contribution by the State. The resignation of Professor Trowbridge and a complete reorganization of the Foundation lost us another year, and then an additional project for a physical-chemical institute necessitated a complete revision of plans.

In 1930 we were at last granted a sum of DM 993,000 towards the building of a research institute. One serious difficulty, however, remained. The foundation was forbidden by statute to help with the building of the lecture hall planned to serve both zoology and botany, and the State had no money for the project—this was, of course, during the great depression. Yet it was clear that working at the new Institute and lecturing at the Old Academy was going to be extremely harmful to all our activities. However, in the end it was proved once again that if the will is there, a way can be found where none seems possible, and by dint of some complicated financial juggling, involving a loan from an insurance company and the participation of the City's Public Works Programme for the Unemployed, the Minister somehow produced the necessary funds. In the upshot, we not only had the most up-to-date zoological institute in Europe by the autumn of 1932, but half a year later, a beautiful lecture hall as well.

AMERICAN JOURNEY, 1930

WHEN during the course of 1929 our project began to look distinctly hopeful, I thought it was time to re-examine our plans with great attention to detail. Naturally I was interested to learn how some of the problems with which I found myself confronted had been solved elsewhere. A journey through the United States in March and April 1930 provided me with an excellent opportunity to do so.

The suggestion for this trip came from Marcella Boveri, whose late husband, the great Theodor Boveri, had been revered by us of the younger generation as one of the founding fathers of our science. I had only met him at congresses and at the Naples station, but when he was offered the directorship of the New Kaiser Wilhelm Institute (now the Max Planck Institute) in 1913, he asked me whether I would be prepared to join him there. Alas, he fell ill and died soon afterwards in 1915 so that the plan came to nothing.

Marcella, *née* O'Grady, was an American biologist who had come to Würzburg for postgraduate studies and had stayed to marry the Professor. After his death she returned to America where she became Professor of Biology at Albertus Magnus College in New Haven, but she returned frequently to Germany to visit her daughter Margret, and our paths had crossed again in later years. Marcella, who liked to talk about her late husband's work and to chat about fellow zoologists on both sides of the Atlantic, became a close friend of ours. She it was who suggested that I should go over some time, and with the energy and enthusiasm that was typical of her she arranged a lecture tour under the auspices of the International Education Board, making light of my qualms as to the inadequacy of my English. Without raising a finger myself, I was one fine day presented with a complete itinerary and lecture list.

Nevertheless, I hesitated to accept, for our youngest off-spring, little Otto (a boy at last!), was not yet 3 months old and very delicate. However, knowing that he would have the best care possible at the clinic of our old friend M. von Pfaundler, I went.

When the steamer *München* on which a berth had been booked for me fell victim to a disastrous fire in New York harbour, I chose to cross on the *York*, scheduled to take 10–11 days for the trip, rather than on the *Bremen,* the then holder of the Blue Riband of the Atlantic, for on the older and smaller vessel I would be so much closer to the sea I loved than in a huge swimming hotel. True enough, we ran into quite a respectable gale with waves that towered (literally for once) above our small but sturdy craft. Being a good sailor I thoroughly enjoyed the howling of the wind, the ever-changing shapes of the waves enveloping the bridge in clouds of spray, and the exciting light effects. To my disappointment there were few animals to be seen apart from gulls, which are always graceful, and the funny little puffins. Once the captain tried to show me some whales, but they were too far away.

On the crossing I employed my time in putting the finishing touches to my lectures. A German-American with whom I had conversed in English asked me whether I intended to lecture in that language. When I replied in the affirmative, he remarked drily: "I don't expect you will be very successful." Fortunately, his dismal prognostication did not worry me overmuch. I was never good at small talk and I suppose the old gentleman would have been equally sceptical about my chances as a lecturer if we had talked in German.

We arrived outside New York on the evening of 10 March after a voyage lasting 12 days, and entered the harbour the following morning. I cannot describe how impressed I was when I saw the famous skyline, the tops of the skyscrapers appearing like mountain peaks above a bank of groundfog. Later I was to be equally over-whelmed by the view at night from the roof of the American Museum of Natural History.

My first destination was New Haven, where Mrs. Boveri, Professor A. G. Harrison, and other members of the faculty received me most cordially. This friendly atmosphere helped me to get through my first lectures; they were: "The sense of hearing in fishes", "The colour vision of fishes and the duplicity theory of vision", and "The language of the bees". Admittedly I felt rather nervous. For I was no more accustomed to reading my lectures from manuscript than to delivering them freely in a foreign language. It all went surprising well, however. Soon I was able to free myself from the tyranny of the prepared text and could improvise when I wanted to.

Briefly, my itinerary was as follows: from New Haven to Harvard in Cambridge, Mass., where G. H. Parker, in particular, shared my interests; then New York with a lecture at Columbia University, followed by one at Cornell University in Ithaca. From there I went to Buffalo on the invitation of Professor P. J. Trudel, who had been my guest at the Munich Institute; with him I visited Niagara Falls. Next I went to Chicago via Ann Arbor, and there saw "zoology in action" in the form of the famous stockyards and meat-processing factories. Fascinated, I watched a pig being transformed into canned meat in one continuous flow.

From Chicago my journey took me to Madison (University of Wisconsin) and then to the University of Iowa where I enjoyed a meeting with Professor Witschi, who had been a pupil of Hertwig's at Munich with me, and finally to Minneapolis, the westernmost point of my tour. As the guest of Professor D. E. Minnich, who had worked for a year at our Institute, I slept in a genuine Bavarian bedstead which he had taken back with him as a souvenir. I was even more impressed by the objects he and his wife had collected during a long stay in China. Their home was indeed a treasure house of beautiful things.

At Bloomington, Indiana, I reached the southernmost point of my itinerary. The sight of flowering Judas trees among the white blossoms of dogwood rising over a carpet of phlox enchanted me. My host, Professor A. C. Kinsey, took me on a memorable excursion to the karstlike caves of the region with their underground rivers and fascinating fauna. Then east again via Columbus and Cleveland (Ohio) and Philadelphia to Princeton, where I was surprised to see Professor Trowbridge. The kind man had come specially from New York to tell me that the Rockefeller Foundation had just voted the funds for the rebuilding of our Institute. I do not think I have often been in better form than on that evening. My last lecture was a paper on the hearing capacity of fish, read to the Annual Convention of the National Academy of Sciences at Washington. With lectures at smaller universities sandwiched in between, there was plenty to do and to see, but thanks to the truly miraculous hospitality of my American friends who seemed to divine all my wishes and provided for my needs without my having to say a word, the tour was no strain but a positive pleasure.

For large parts of the journey I was taken by car and therefore saw a great deal more of the country than I could have done from a train. Often I was struck by the difference in technological standards between my own country and America: for instance, when we passed a lonely farm where not only a car, but a private aeroplane stood ready at the gate; or when I tried in vain to *walk* down from my bedroom to the dining room on one of the few occasions I stayed at a hotel, and discovered that all stairs were fire escapes ending at emergency exits on the first floor—Americans, of course, never dreaming of descending otherwise than by lift. From Ithaca I had an opportunity to visit the reservation of the Onondaga Indians. As a former admirer of the stories by Charles Fennimore Cooper and his German counterpart Karl May, I was looking forward to a glimpse of the old romantic magic. Alas, these descendants of a mighty tribe lived in ramshackle wooden houses and not in wigwams, wore shabby European clothing and no feather head-dresses, and, ultimate indignity—rode in incredibly dilapidated motor-cars and not on fiery steeds.

Perhaps the eagerness of my hosts to show me historical places, the oldest houses in town, the site of some event in the Civil War, and other landmarks of their past, actually enhanced in me the impression of the country's youthfulness. Looking at the university city of Madison I should not have guessed that 100 years ago the place had been a primeval forest, and that 70 years ago bloody battles had been fought with the Red Indians on that very spot. The Indian mounds close by, grassy elevations in the shape of tortoises or birds which had served as places of worship to the rightful inhabitants of the continent, impressed me deeply.

The conquest of the country by the Whites must have been a

rough, tough, and brutal affair. But nowadays it is the gentleness of their manners that strikes the visitor to America. In all those weeks I never heard an unkind word, not even between Americans. If, say, something was missing that was needed at a lecture, or if a technician did not turn up until the last moment, no one would show signs of impatience and, even less, anger. In the end, things usually came right. "It would be foolish of the film operator to be late," Professor Harrison remarked quietly on one occasion, "he knows he would be sacked at once." This mentality is very different from ours, but no doubt it is salutary.

The evenings were usually spent with the families of my respective hosts, a cheerful fire supplying warmth and a cosy atmosphere without any need for alcoholic drinks (for this was the era of prohibition). Prohibition, however, did not prevent me from getting tipsy for the first and only time in my life since people with rather more money than respect for the law could get as much of the stuff as they liked. It happened in New York at some smart lunch on a scorching hot day, where I downed a marvellous cocktail on an empty stomach. My behaviour must have been rather odd, but fortunately for me, the other guests were all old friends.

As I had hoped, my visits to so many American universities provided me with plenty of new ideas for our own building plans. The institutes varied tremendously. Some were very beautiful and practical, others old-fashioned and poorly equipped. But they all had one thing in common.

Whereas in Germany there is usually one Professor of Zoology who runs his department with the aid of a few lecturers and, if he is fortunate, one assistant professor, there were invariably several professors, sometimes as many as 12 or 15, in each zoological department. One of the advantages of such a system is, of course, the chance it gives to gifted young scientists of getting to the top eventually. With us even people with excellent scientific records quite often never reach the consummation of an academic career. Hence many excellent men prefer to go into teaching or industry and are lost to science.*

But, of course, this is not the only value of a greater number of

---

* The above was written in 1956. Since then there has been a change for the better in German universities.

senior posts. Their other importance lies in the expansion and diversification of scientific research they make possible.

Once Germany led the world in histology, comparative anatomy and physiology, theory of evolution, genetics, etc., but not now. And unless those in authority realize very soon that science needs to be one of the chief concerns of the State, we shall never be able to recover our lead. The position is similar in other branches of learning.

The fact that the professors at an American institute of zoology can specialize in, say, general zoology, morphology, theory of evolution, general and comparative physiology, genetics, histology, hormones, etc., is, however, not entirely free from dangers. Although in some departments the various specialists are constantly in touch with each other, imparting their findings to their colleagues and learning from them all the time, in others they keep themselves in water-tight compartments and seem to walk through the exciting landscape of science in blinkers. Of course, there are such people everywhere, but they are a greater menace where a generous endowment of posts may lead either to fruitful collaboration or to narrow over-specialization.

This tendency to specialize is perhaps favoured by the set-up of American academic training methods which I think resemble too much those of secondary schools, at any rate in my subject—I cannot speak about others. I believe that in our Greater Zoological Practical, German students have a better opportunity to acquire independence and self-reliance in scientific thinking before they are expected to tackle research problems unaided. Admittedly the quality of our training has also deteriorated with an increase in students that is not matched by a corresponding increase in teaching staff.

More than anything else, I admired the libraries at most universities. They rightly take great pride in them. Not only have they large holdings and generous endowments, and are quiet and pleasant to work in, but—the most important point—they provide rapid service. In many large libraries one would get one's book within 3 minutes from handing in one's order slip.

These are but a few salient impressions from my short trip which brought me many pleasurable moments and not a single unpleasant hour.

AT THE NEW INSTITUTE

WE OWE an immense debt of gratitude to Dr. Th. Kollmann, the architect of our new Institute. That the building turned out as we had envisaged it is entirely due to his exceptional experience in the building of laboratories, his outstanding ability as an architect, and his willingness to fall in with all our wishes down to the position of the last light switch. At all times he would be at our disposal for consultations on major points or minor details, anxious to find the best possible solution. Working with him was sheer joy.

Nevertheless our hearts were heavy when, in the autumn of 1932, we were leaving our familiar rooms at the Old Academy where the very air seemed saturated with tradition. At the same time we were buoyed up by the expectation of bringing to life the most modern, the most beautiful zoological institute in Europe, and confident that we should be able to carry the old spirit with us into our new quarters—seeing that its very embodiment, old Professor Hertwig, enthusiastically joined in the move despite his 82 years.

As the Rockefeller Foundation had very wisely made its grant conditional on the provision of adequate working funds by the Bavarian authorities, we were assured of enough money for our running expenses. Moreover, our new budget provided for an increase in technical staff and raised the number of scientific assistants from 3 to 6. The post of First Assistant which carried the title of Conservator—an anachronism from the time of museum zoology—had always been a senior pensionable post. This had enabled us to attract a scientist whose knowledge and approach was complementary to that of the head of the department. At the old Institute, its incumbent had been J. Seiler, a cytologist and geneticist. After he left for Zürich we were joined at the new Institute by J. Holtfreter, an evolutionary physiologist, who now, like so many of his countrymen since the days of National Socialism, works for the greater glory of the United States. In the same manner we tried to fill the other assistants' posts with men representing different aspects of our science. This is the only way we can compensate for the lack of an adequate number of professorial endowments in the manner of our American counterparts. Especially those assistants who become "private lecturers" (*Privatdozenten*, cf. p. 52) tend to form their own little groups of pupils and to act as heads of sections.

FIG. 24. The Old Academy. Our Institute lay at the back, towards the gardens. The front section shown here housed part of the zoological collections. The building was completely destroyed in the Second World War. (*Photograph Dr. Ecke, ca. 1931.*)

In order that people working in different parts of our vast building should not lose contact with each other, a pleasant staff room was part of the plan where a cheerful crowd would gather for tea and a chat in the afternoon. There were also facilities for preparing a simple meal. It was a good place for making friends; a place where you could talk and relax, and where, quite often, you would pick up some useful scientific ideas.

A zoological institute must not only be designed for the well-being of its human occupants but equally for that of the animals they work with. We had culture rooms on all floors, an aquarium, an insectarium, a tropical house and, in the grounds, stabling and fenced paddocks as well as pools large and small with running or stagnant water. In the basement there was a spacious tank providing an even temperature all the year round and other environmental conditions favourable for cave-dwelling animals such as the interesting cave salamander, *Proteus anguineus*, from the karst

FIG. 25. The new Zoological Institute of Munich University, erected 1931–1932 with funds supplied by the Rockefeller Foundation.

region. It goes without saying that the social insects were not forgotten. There was provision for a bees'-house, and there were special island sites surrounded by water designed for ant colonies, where these lively little fellows would be able to busy themselves as they pleased around their nests yet would be unable to escape. How marvellous it was that at last we were to have suitable quarters for all the creatures we were interested in.

Before the bees'-house was erected, however, it was suggested to me that I should have the garden surveyed by water diviners, as bees would not thrive above a subterranean watercourse. Water-divining was at that time a hotly debated topic and was even studied

I

scientifically at one of the university's institutes. I myself was sceptical but, knowing nothing of the subject either by experience or from literature, I felt it was best to judge by facts. From colleagues interested in the matter I obtained the addresses of five water-diviners who, I was assured, were thoroughly reliable men. I asked each of them separately to examine the garden and to enter his findings on a plan. When they had finished—each one of them had located water-courses which criss-crossed the area in all directions—I transferred their several findings on to one plan with coloured inks. The five patterns were completely different; not once did two lines of different colour coincide. I therefore put my bees'-house in the place I considered most convenient, and never bothered about water-divining again.

The new lecture hall was also beautifully equipped and contained all kinds of modern teaching aids: movable tables for experiments, a good epidiascope, a micro-projector, projectors for 8 and 16 mm film, and a special room to stage demonstrations.

For the first years of its existence the new hall formed a link between ourselves and the botanists, who used it for their more general lectures, for which their own institute at Nymphenburg was too out of the way. Our relations were particularly close while Fritz von Wettstein represented the *Scientia amabilis* in Munich, for he was an old friend of mine from student days with whom I shared many interests. Unfortunately he soon left for the Kaiser Wilhelm Institute (cf. p. 111) which he thought offered him better opportunities for undisturbed scientific work in troubled times.

Of the many guest workers who came to our Institute I want to mention only Geheimrat A. Denker, formerly the director of the ear clinic at Halle who in his leisure time worked on the ears of animals and had, *inter alia*, produced a painstaking study on the ears of parrots. He was greatly interested in our work on the hearing of fishes and, after his retirement, devoted his remaining energies to this research.

Through him I was made an honorary member of the Society of Otolaryngologists, the only one, as he emphasized, who was not a member of the medical profession. We were at Brunnwinkl when Denker announced his forthcoming visit. Although I admit I had an inkling of what was in the wind, I never thought that he would take the matter so seriously. Yet when he came, he was dressed in ceremonial black while I sat opposite him in my holiday attire, the traditional leather shorts of the region with a rustic coat to match, and my wife wore her Austrian "Dirndl dress" when she poured our coffee. He obviously would have liked a bigger audience and asked whether any of my relatives were staying at Brunnwinkl. Before I realized what he had in mind he rose from his seat and, standing stiff and upright, delivered a long and carefully composed address in impeccable style. When it came to the handing over of the diploma, I, too, had to stand up, my bare knees and casual get-up contrasting strangely with the solemn attire of our guest. How I wish someone could have photographed us at that moment. The rest of the afternoon, however, passed pleasantly enough.

Though I am in no way mechanically minded, I decided in 1936 to buy a car (or rather my wife decided). The great distance between our home and the Institute made some means of fast transport almost a necessity. We both learned to drive. As soon as my wife had passed her test (she took a little longer than I did) she handed me her licence and asked me to lock it away safely since she did not want to lose a document which it had cost her so much effort to gain. She never touched a steering wheel again. My own test was distinctly tinged with zoology. The beginning was not too auspicious—the car refused to start. Seeing I had not thought of the ignition key, this was not really surprising. After that, however, it all went swimmingly around a few street corners. Instead of testing my skill in more difficult situations or asking me technical questions (of which I was terrified) the examiner wanted to know whether it was true that fleas were dying out. We discussed this absorbing topic until there was no longer time for anything else.

What a boon the car has been ever since! The time it saved, the field work it made possible, not to speak of the beautiful holidays it allowed us to take. The most important thing for me was, however, that it enabled me to get to my beloved Brunnwinkl, my favourite place of work, in less than 3 hours.

Many people in other walks of life find it difficult to believe that university teachers have 3 months' vacation in the summer and another two at Easter, but those who make envious or sarcastic remarks completely misunderstand the situation. Few professors are likely to spend their holidays in idleness. For most of us they are the principal time in which to do research, for in term time there is so much lecturing, supervising, and administration to be

Fig. 26.   Father and son practising zoology. Outside the garden door of our house at Harlaching, *ca.* 1932.

got through that we can rarely do more than carry out some previously planned experiments. Basically the work of a scientist is no less creative work than that of the artist, and can no more be forced into "normal office hours". It requires freedom for undisturbed concentration, unremitting attention to exploratory experiments, and long periods of searching thought. For all this, we need the "vacs.".

I am sure the students need them too, at any rate the better ones among them. What they have learned in term time, rushing from one lecture to the next, needs to be recapitulated and inwardly digested at leisure before it can form the basis for further independent reading and a deepening of the understanding. In some countries, for instance in the United States, vacations are much less generous. This is in line with their teaching methods which resemble more those of our secondary schools; it may be a good thing for the average or poor student. But I feel convinced that for the *élite*, the future leaders of thought on whom all scientific progress depends, our method is preferable, for only in this way can we train our students to think for themselves. If we did not possess this advantage in scientific training, the achievements of German science would lag behind those of other, more affluent, countries far more than they do now.

In the course of our research into the hearing of fishes the question arose whether minnows are capable of recognizing the direction of sound. We ourselves can do this with fair accuracy. But as the anatomy of fishes differs from ours, we cannot simply assume that they localize the source of a sound in the same way as we do. Because of the reflection of sound waves from their walls, aquaria are unsuitable for experiments on this point. We tried to put our insectary under water, thus producing quite a sizeable "lake", but even there the echoing from the walls was a serious obstacle.

But at Brunnwinkl there was a real lake, and in it there were many swarms of minnows. And as I had just finished a series of experiments on bees, I decided to study this problem in the field. My experiments there led to the conclusion that minnows cannot localize sound. This result was not unexpected and therefore not particularly exciting. Yet there were surprises of a different nature, which opened up new fields of discovery.

The swarm of minnows we used for our experiments had gradually become so tame that they would take food from our hands. They always came to the same spot on a shallow stretch near the shore. I was anxious to find out whether the same individuals turned up day by day. I therefore caught one of the little fishes. To mark it I severed a certain nerve by the prick of a needle, an operation which causes its tail to go dark for a number of days, and released it again. It did not seem at all upset and joined its fellows. But then a strange thing happened: instead of swimming happily about, the fishes seemed to gather anxiously close to the shallow bottom, putting their heads together as if they were whispering to each other, and all of a sudden the whole swarm disappeared in the depths. They would not come near again and were not tempted by the most appetizing food. It took much patience and a number of days before they lost their fear again. What had happened? The following summer I tried to find out.

The most plausible assumption seemed to be that the injured minnow had warned the others. Considering that they could hear so well, there was no reason why they should not also be able to communicate with each other by sounds. After I had tamed another swarm, I killed one of the little fishes by decapitation, and returned it to the lake close to the rest of the swarm. Though there was now obviously no possibility of such a direct warning, there was the same almost instantaneous reaction of fright and sudden flight. Was it caused by the sight of the dead body? No, for the same effect could be obtained with a fish cut into such small pieces that its former shape was unrecognizable, and even with the filtered water in which it had lain. I concluded that their behaviour was caused by a warning substance released when a fish was injured.

These experiments, which had taken much longer than this short account would lead one to expect, had frightened away so many swarms of minnows that we had to spend long hours in a boat searching the shallows near the shore for a swarm we could work with. We therefore continued our research in the laboratory.

It was not difficult to tame swarms of minnows in a large aquarium which contained suitable hiding places made of stone to which they could flee when frightened, and observation there was certainly a good deal easier and less time-consuming than in the waters of Lake Wolfgang for, if one swarm was frightened, it could be replaced by another without delay.

These experiments confirmed that a warning substance was released when the skin of a minnow was punctured. The other members of the swarm were able to perceive the merest trace and to react to quite incredible dilutions. It caused them to flee and to remain on the alert for a very long time. When a pike (their chief enemy) catches a minnow, its sharp teeth will invariably puncture the skin. The minute quantities of an olfactory substance which thereby get into the water are enough to warn the fellows of the unfortunate victim, for their sense of smell is acute; in this way they are saved from being gobbled up one by one.

This remarkable system of "life insurance" is, however, not universal in the world of fish. Perch, for instance, will devour a dismembered individual of their own species with relish. Perhaps they do not need this kind of protection. But what about other peaceful and defenceless gregarious fish?

There is a little lake, or rather tarn, in the woods just above Lake Wolfgang where white fish of the species *Squalius cephalus* abound. When I fed them with maize, which they love, they soon lost their fear. I then picked up a length of rusty guttering which happened to be lying there and laid it on the sloping bank with one end in the water. Through this improvised channel I poured a measured quantity of *Squalius* skin extract into the water and waited, stopwatch in hand, for the reaction of the fish, which was strong and immediate. Pleased with the result, I turned to go, when my eyes fell on an old yokel who must have watched me all along from behind a tree. I shall never forget the expression on his face. He obviously thought me quite mad. For who in his senses would pour some drops of water into the lake through an old drain pipe and then start to scribble furiously, looking at his watch all the time? I did not disabuse him.

At any rate, I had proved that this method of improving the chances of survival in the face of rapacious predators was not specific to minnows. It now remained to be seen whether it was common to all peaceful gregarious fish. Prolonged investigations by myself and my pupils showed that warning substances occur with all cyprinids (to which nearly three-quarters of all our freshwater fish belong) but that they are not found with all peaceful gregarious fish.

Nature in her inventiveness scorns schematic solutions, and has thought of a variety of protective devices to ensure the survival of a species against terrific odds.

Minnows have a very acute sense of smell which is by no means attuned to the warning substance only. Their "nose" equals that of dogs, enabling them to distinguish and to recognize not only different species of fish, but also individuals of their own species. Their sense of taste is also very much better than ours. If it is further considered that they can see all the colours we can, plus ultraviolet which we cannot, that their hearing is excellent, and that they possess a wonderfully sensitive lateral organ for the perception of slight movements in the surrounding water, it will not come as a surprise that these fish with their marvellous sensory equipment were among our favourites in studies concerning the comparative physiology of the senses, and that we were examining them in every possible way. At the same time we carried out experiments with a great variety of insects. How we enjoyed bringing into play all the facilities our new Institute had to offer and making use of its many potentialities.

These researches take us already into the Nazi era. Even at the time of the move into our new quarters we felt the shadow of political events and wondered anxiously whether we should really be able to enjoy our beautiful new Institute. During the first few years we were not troubled. But by and by difficulties arose and became more serious as time went on.

I remember vividly a visit from Richard Goldschmidt who came to look over the new building. Already, there were political informers everywhere, and it is characteristic of the state of affairs which plagued us at the time that not before we had reached the deepest cellar recesses, and he was alone with me and the cave salamander, did Goldschmidt dare to speak openly: movements of this sort could only survive by constantly increasing the violence of their doctrines and actions. He personally did not wish to stay and await these excesses. He was going to America while he could do so of his own free will.

If the universities had presented a united front, they might perhaps have put up a successful resistance. But many professors subscribed to the new measures, be it from caution or from conviction. And soon there was no doubt that any serious resistance spelled self-annihilation.

It was not long before the loss of our freedom made itself felt at home and at work.

In 1933 the notorious tax of DM 1000 for a permit to visit Austria (designed to bring that country to its knees by ruining its tourist trade) prevented me, for the first time in my life, from going to Brunnwinkl in the summer. We spent some pleasant weeks at Castle Lautrach, the lovely Bavarian summer residence of the late Dr. Hermann Anschütz-Kaempfe, the inventor of the gyroscopic compass, whose widow had invited us.

At the Institute I was denied the right of freely choosing my own staff, something that is absolutely essential for harmonious team work. The assistants we got were chosen for political motives. They were meant to spy on us and to make sure we toed the line. Soon, not only assistants, but lecturers and professors likewise, were appointed for political services rendered. No one bothered to find out what *we* thought about their scientific qualifications.

Practical goals were to be kept in the foreground of our scientific research far more than in the past. Science for science's sake, the pure striving after truth, received but scant encouragement. Moreover, we were hampered by increasing isolation from abroad. There was no understanding of the truth that science is international and cannot thrive behind barriers.

Vexations, large and small, became constantly more numerous. Occasionally they were incredibly petty. One day I was summoned to the Ministry on a charge of cruelty to animals at our Institute. It was one of the crassest contradictions of that time that the National Socialist movement, which probably caused as much or more human suffering than any other dictatorship, championed the protection of animals. What had happened at our Institute? Students had reported that one or the other of the earth worms which had been used in the practical had wriggled a little on being dissected in spite of the preceding anaesthetizing with alcohol. I asked why no one proceeded against the anglers who impaled live worms on their hooks without any sort of narcotic. The reply was: this was done for food production and was in the national interest. I had to explain at some length about the primitive nervous system of these worms and their—presumably—very low level of perceptions of any sort before I was permitted to continue my practical on the basic facts of zoology.

As Goldschmidt had prophesied, things became more irksome from year to year. But soon vexations and pinpricks paled in significance before far more horrible events.

THE SECOND WORLD WAR

THOSE who kept their eyes open and were not taken in by phrases knew that war was imminent. The psychology of men and women who had experienced the First World War and yet were willing to let themselves be hurled into another was, to me, an unfathomable mystery. Now this horrible misery and wretchedness would have to be lived through all over again, like a ghastly theme with endless variations. The situation was indeed, tragic. A victory for National Socialism would mean the triumph of Wrong. Their defeat would spell equal suffering for the righteous and the guilty.

Preparation had evidently been thorough and organization was brilliant. This was equally evident from the initial successes of the blitzkrieg and the smooth switchover to war-time controls on the home front. Ration cards for foodstuffs were introduced overnight. I recollect that on reading the announcement in the paper I had a distinct sensation of emptiness in my stomach—a psychological experience not then in accordance with the physiological facts.

This is not the place to discuss the historical events that led eventually to Germany's crushing defeat. I mean to record no more than a few personal experiences. There was hardly a family that was not drawn into the maelstrom.

The work of our Institute was threatened in two ways. For one thing, scientific projects which did not hold out the hope of immediate practical benefits had little prospect of survival in a prolonged war. For the other, I was far from being *persona grata* with the people in power. In 1941 it even looked as if I should have to leave the Institute, and my premature retirement seemed inescapable.

That we were allowed to carry on with comparatively few restrictions and even substantial help from the authorities we owed, on the one hand, to the devoted efforts of well-meaning and influential friends and, on the other, to the honey-bees.

In the years 1940–1942 the hives of Germany and other European countries were hit by a calamitous epidemic which at its height wiped out several hundred thousands of hives. This meant not only a severe reduction of the honey crop, but an equally grave situation for agriculture and fruit growing. For, as is well known, the bees are the most important pollinators of many crop plants. During a time when food was in short supply this failure of the bees was therefore a twofold catastrophe.

The pathogen causing the disease is a microscopic unicellular parasite in the bees' digestive tract called *Nosema apis*. These minute organisms can frequently be found in the bees' intestines without causing any ill effects, but at other times they suddenly become virulent for unknown reasons, multiply prodigiously, and cause severe mortality.

It is a universal experience. The less is known about a disease, the more remedies are being peddled. In this case, too, innumerable preparations were sold to the bee-keepers, but without exception they were a complete waste of money.

In this situation a special "Nosema Council" was formed to try to tackle the problem. Its chairman, a man of influence in matters of food production, who knew my work and was aware of the dangers that threatened my position, succeeded in obtaining for me an official research assignment from the Ministry of Food to investigate the disease. We were given adequate funds and the necessary staff, and a certain freedom of movement (literally, too, in the form of petrol coupons). I was even allowed to get some key workers I needed back from the front. For myself, I was glad to have an occupation which was in accordance with the seriousness of the times and which if successful would benefit bee-keepers the world over.

Our first step was to test the existing remedies on caged individuals and whole populations. Not one was any good. We also tested without success many other preparations which might conceivably have a chemotherapeutic effect. With the help of bee-keepers' organizations we instituted an observation service to find out which climatic or environmental factors favoured the disease or inhibited it. When it appeared that the supply of pollen, that is to say, the protein nutrition of the bees, was somehow connected with susceptibility, my assistant, Professor Ruth Beutler, undertook to study this particular problem. But because there were obviously so many basic questions which needed to be cleared up first and which would in all probability take years to solve, we knew that we could not hope for quick results. And in fact we did not succeed in producing a satisfactory solution of the problem while the war lasted.

After a short while our terms of reference were enlarged in a direction which was much closer to my own scientific interests but equally of great practical importance. It was learned from Russian journals that large-scale trials were afoot in that country which aimed at stimulating the bees to visit any desired crop of agricultural importance by feeding them sugar water scented with the smell of the plants in question. The method was based on my earlier experiments on the bees' sense of smell and language. In fact, my then adviser, Guido Bamberger, had put these ideas into practice many years earlier. I remember his telling me that once when he and some others had moved their hives to a region of rich bee pasture, he had taken a few blossoms of the chief honey plant, sprayed them with honey and sugar water, and placed them at the flight holes of his hives. The first bees finding the blossoms on leaving the hive alerted their fellow workers by dancing and sent them off to find the flowers the smell of which adhered to their hairy bodies. In this way they were the first in the field, and Bamberger had the richest honey crop of the lot. He had invented odour guidance. In the past I had repeatedly tried to interest the bee-keeping community in the matter, but without success. Now, the Russian experiments were to be tested and followed up.

Conditions were favourable. With the active support of the bee-keepers' official organization we were able to carry out field experiments wherever and whenever we wanted. Only the general collapse at the end of the war put a stop to our activities.

The method was completely successful with red clover. The seed for this important fodder legume was grown chiefly in the Rhineland and in East Prussia, but crops were variable and often poor, for the blossoms cannot bear seed without insect pollination, and their natural pollinators, the bumble-bees, are never sufficiently numerous to cope with whole fields. Honey-bees are not normally much interested in red clover because their tongues are not quite long enough to enable them to extract all the nectar from the bottom of the long narrow calyx of these flowers. But by giving them food that smells of clover, they can be tricked into believing that the honey source is worth their effort. We were able to perfect a practical method which raised mean yields by about 40 per cent and secured regular crops for the farmer. Trials with other important agricultural crops were promising but were not completed.

As a means of increasing honey crops from a number of pasture plants, odour guidance was highly successful because foraging intensity was greatly stimulated by scented feeding. In large-scale trials with white clover, rape, turnips, heather, and a thistle, *Cirsium oleraceum*, average yields were increased by 25–65 per cent.

The matter would need further study and practical promotion, but the bee research institutes and bee-keepers' training schools whose job this would be are as short of money and staff as the universities themselves. It is apparently not realized that parsimony in matters of research is very expensive in the long run.

Our own work was overshadowed by the events of the war and by the uncertainty about my personal position. For some time we had received ominous demands to produce certain documents relating to the ancestry of my maternal grandmother, documents we knew we were unable to supply. In January 1941 the chancellery of the university made known to me the following communication from the Bavarian Ministry:

> The Reichsministry of Education has ascertained that Dr. K. v. Frisch, ordinary Professor at Munich University, is of mixed descent in the second degree. It is therefore the intention of the Reichsminister for Education, Science and Learning that he should be retired in accordance with para. 72 DBG. I shall be obliged if you will communicate this intention to Professor von Frisch.

Hans Spemann, whom I told of this communication, replied at once.

> My dear respected friend,
>
> I do not want to put down on paper what I feel when I read and reread your letter. But I want to entreat you: Don't let this poison enter your soul! So people like your mother should not be allowed to dwell among us! It is enough to make one despair! But not, I hasten to say, of the issue in your own particular case. . . .
>
> With kindest regards, to yourself and your wife, from both of us.
>
> > Yours,
> >
> > H. SPEMANN

He wrote at once to Reichsminister Rust but never received a reply.

Other fellow scientists and several people well disposed towards me of whose existence I had not even been aware also tried to intervene on my behalf. The fact that I had not been retired outright, but had only received an intimation of intent, gave us a little time.

Since legally there was no necessity for removing me from office —others similarly placed had been left alone—we thought there must be a special reason. We found out that I was accused of an attempt to conceal the non-Arian descent of my maternal grandmother. I could prove that this was untrue. When submitting her baptismal certificate I had pointed out, as early as 1937, that her descent was not clear. Though the Minister of Education admitted as much on 2 October 1941, his communication addressed to the Bavarian Ministry did not leave me any hope, for the last paragraph read as follows:

> Under the law on the Civil Service* there never was nor is there now a provision which would make it incumbent on me to retain Professor von Frisch in office. He was not an established civil servant on 1 August 1914. The fact that he fulfilled the conditions for establishment at that time does not move me to use my discretion to treat him as if he had been. I shall be obliged if you will inform Professor v. Frisch accordingly and if you will let me have your proposals for retiring him.

Apparently they were pleased to have a reason for getting rid of me.

---

* This law applied to university teachers.

And yet it did not come to pass. What happened behind the scenes I do not know, of course, in any detail. For months all news that reached me by devious or direct channels contained not a grain of hope. But in the end some friends whose opinions carried weight because of their economic or political eminence obtained a reversal of the decision by using their influence at the Ministry of Food and at Party headquarters. On 27 July 1942 the Minister of Education wrote:

> Acting in agreement with the Director of the Party Secretariat I have decided not to pursue the matter of Professor von Frisch's retirement until after the war.

After that, I ceased to worry.

To keep my élan for my work alive I tried to bury myself in it completely, taking as little notice as I could help of the events around me, which no one could influence anyway. During the first years of the Third Reich my wife kept a diary, but later she burned that highly compromising document at my request. A pity, in a way.

However, there are also some pleasanter memories.

Through the introduction of mutual friends we occasionally spent a few days in a small guest house at the beautiful mountain village of Leogang near Saalfelden (Salzburg) run by Baron Th. von Seyffertitz and his family. At a time when one did not dare to speak openly at the Institute or even among so-called friends, his house was indeed a haven in which we could breathe again and regain our strength. This friendship of the war years has survived into better days.

Two joyful events stand out particularly from the dark canvas of those days.

On 29 March 1943 our youngest daughter Leni was married in Munich to Ekkehard, a son of our old friends, the Pflügers from Rostock, whom we were especially delighted to welcome as our first son-in-law. Alas, the happiness of the young couple was tragically shortlived, for Ekkehard fell victim to senseless slaughter in the last few days of the war. Six months after the first wedding we celebrated another at Brunnwinkl. On 23 October 1943, on one of those incredibly beautiful autumn days when the sky and the lake vied with the tree-clad hills in colourful splendour, the wedding party of my eldest daughter Johanna crossed the lake to the parish church of St. Gilgen in gaily decorated *Traundln*, the local flat-bottomed boats rowed by standing oarsmen rather in the manner of Venetian gondolas (Fig. 27). The bridegroom was my pupil and assistant, Dr. Theodor Schreiner, who thus be-

FIG. 27. Return from the wedding across Lake Wolfgang. Dr. Theodor and Johanna Schreiner. *Oarsmen:* my brother Otto and my son Otto. 23 October 1943.

came the second zoologist in our family circle, not counting our son Otto, who was clearly destined eventually to become a third.

The incorporation of Austria into the German Reich brought us one great advantage: it made travelling between Munich and Brunnwinkl very much easier, so that even in the midst of the war we were able to take a dozen or two students on excursions around Lake Wolfgang and the Schafberg (Fig. 28). These pleasant scientific rambles stand out like oases in the barren desert of those years. Incidentally, my museum, as a comprehensive collection of the local fauna and flora, acquired a new usefulness in this connection.

Soon this easy accessibility of our summer residence was to become even more important.

FIG. 28.   Descent from the Schafberg. Excursion by the Munich Zoological Institute, July 1940. View of St. Gilgen and Lake Wolfgang. *In the centre:* Brunnwinkl.

When Italy had fallen, Munich became severely exposed to Allied bombing. Our work was greatly hampered by the incessant alerts and the constant danger even before our Institute received a direct hit. I therefore arranged for the evacuation of part of the staff and the valuable equipment to Brunnwinkl, where two of the houses of our little colony were converted into laboratories. Later, on 5 August 1944, about half of the Institute personnel moved

K

to the quiet bay of Lake Wolfgang, and there we were able to keep faith with our vocation even during the last troubled year of the war. Other makeshift laboratories were established in nearby Weissenbach am Attersee and at Straubing. Those who could not or would not go away looked after things in Munich as best they could, and I myself was travelling to and fro, trying to keep the threads in my hand.

My wife had taken up permanent residence at Brunnwinkl. In our house at Harlaching there lived beside myself my daughter Maria, who was employed in the secretariat of the Chemical Institute, my daughter Johanna and her husband Theo who worked in Munich at the time, and a young couple who had been bombed out of their flat.

About noon on 12 July 1944 Munich suffered a heavy air raid. When at last we emerged from our underground shelter at the Institute I drove Ruth Beutler home in my car, intending to return almost immediately. At her suggestion I drove back via Harlaching. I found the approach to our road blocked by splintered trees, and on both its sides I could see flames spurting from the houses. Where ours ought to have been there was a gaping hole. A heap of rubble was all that was left after it had been hit by two high-explosive bombs. Flames issued from the door of the basement where my library had been stored (fortunately I had taken part of it to Brunnwinkl). No help was available, since the neighbours were busy with their own fires. Nor was there any water. It took days for the conflagration to die down. The tattered trees in our garden were festooned with torn cushions and even a bucket hung from a branch, blown there by the force of the explosion which also, apparently, had completely destroyed my writing desk, for I found my wife's letters, which had been kept in it, strewn all over the place. This was rather awkward, for they were not suitable for the eyes of our neighbour, the leader of the local Party group and an ardent Nazi. I picked up what I could, and to this day many a letter ingrained with dust and grit serves as a curious memento of those grim hours. Providentially, nobody had been at home at the time of the raid.

My daughter Maria and I found refuge for the night with some kind friends who presented me at once with a brand new toothbrush and face flannel. I have not often been so pleased with any present—I suppose because this gesture of friendly solicitude gave me that sense of comfort I so much needed at the time. The loss of really valuable things somehow hardly registered in the midst of the fateful blows which rained down on us from all sides.

On the following day, 13 July 1944, another noon raid caused severe damage to our Institute. Thereafter, systematic work at Munich was out of the question and, as I had no home left, I came to town for short visits only, especially as I could carry on my research work at Brunnwinkl with many members of my staff. We were hampered only by the general food shortage which compelled us to spend a good deal of our time wrestling with the soil.

In peace-time each house of our colony, of course, had had its vegetable garden but for pleasure rather than out of necessity. Now, however, it was no longer a question of a preference for fresh vegetables or newly dug potatoes, but simply the choice between going hungry and having enough to eat. By turning all our meadow land into potato fields and vegetable plots we managed to feed the whole community but we all had to work hard, hoeing and watering, and learning about the right way of growing things.

Those members of the Institute who remained in Munich tried heroically to keep our building from complete destruction in the times of trouble and turmoil that followed.

WORKING QUIETLY AT BRUNNWINKL,
1945–1946

ONE fine day in May 1945 we stood on a little knoll outside our hamlet and watched the first American armoured cars drive through St. Gilgen en route from Salzburg to Ischl. It was a great relief to know they were Americans, for the Russian front had been moving steadily nearer from the other side, and for a time it was touch and go who would reach us first.

Just then Johanna, our eldest daughter who lived with us at Brunnwinkl, was daily expecting her first baby. On our way to the hospital in nearby St. Gilgen an American armoured car barred our way. Fortunately the officer in charge, taking in the situation at a glance, allowed us to pass, and a few hours later our first grandson, Peter Schreiner, was born safe and sound amidst the noise and bustle of an occupying army settling into the village.

The first days of the occupation were full of incident and excitement. There were innumerable strict rules, and quite often our homes were being searched by soldiers with rifles at the ready. We lived in constant fear that the military might requisition our houses for the troops. So when one fine day in June an American jeep with four officers stopped in front of our home, we were not a little worried. However, the man who got out first did not inquire about billets but asked after me and my honey-bees. My wife directed him to the observation hives, and there, for the time being, he remained. He was Professor A. D. Hasler, biologist at the University of Wisconsin, who was staying in Salzburg to investigate war damage. His fellow officers turned out to be equally harmless. I do not remember much about them, except that one young man, despite his American uniform, went by the typically Austrian name of "Plunder Franzl" and was a wood carver from the Tyrol, and that they all were delighted with the fresh vegetables we put before them for lunch. These were as welcome to them as their tins of meat and sweetmeats, of which they were heartily tired, were to us. Hasler came often to our house that summer; we became fast friends, and later visited each other in our laboratories. He made it possible for me to travel to Munich occasionally and visit the Institute despite the fact that on the restoration of Austrian independence the German frontier had become hermetically closed to civilians. Even with a military pass the journey was not exactly easy, and I would consider myself in luck if I found a place in some dirty open coal truck of an empty goods train.

The cellars of our Rockefeller institute had remained fairly intact, and this meant, fortunately, that most of our library and valuable equipment which had been stored there, so far as it had not been evacuated, was safe. The rest of the building was in a bad way. The roof was completely destroyed by fire, and apart from three or four rooms on the ground floor, which were just barely usable, all the laboratories were gutted.

Nevertheless, my staff had to return to Munich in the autumn. I myself stayed on for the time being. I had no home to go to, nor was there any prospect of taking up scientific work at the Institute in the near future, and just then I was most anxious not to waste my time. For during the last summer I had seen things with my bees that were more exciting than any of my earlier discoveries.

We had known for about 20 years that successful foragers impart to their fellow workers the news of a promising food source by dancing on the honeycombs in the hive, and that the specific odour adhering to the dancers informs the other bees of the type of flower they have to look for. I had wondered at the time whether the foragers communicated simultaneously a message on distance and direction of the food source, but had dropped the idea as too fantastic. I assumed that the alerted bees would first search the neighbourhood of the hive and go gradually farther afield until they found the flowers with the desired scent (cf. p. 73).

On 2 August 1944 I had for the first time established a food source (dishes containing sugar water scented with lavender) at a distance of 160 yards from the hive. In order to see where the alerted bees which had not yet been there would search, I had placed one lavender-scented dish close to the hive and another close to the food source. I imagined that the bees who issued forth as a result of the dances would first look near the hive and later search in ever-widening circles. To my surprise this was by no means what actually happened. The scented dish near the hive was hardly noticed: it was the distant dish that was soon buzzing with bees. Was it conceivable that their "language" should have a "word" for "distance"?

In order to find out, I arranged for groups of foragers from the same hive to be active at the same time at two different feeding places situated respectively 12 and 280 yards from the hive. The bees were all numbered individually and, in addition, the "home" team received a blue spot on their abdomen and the "away" team a red one. After these preparations I opened the observation hive, hoping to find a difference between the dances of the two groups that human eyes could discern.

There was indeed such a difference, and one that was quite unmistakable. To my intense surprise the "blue" bees from the nearby feeding place danced the round dance, and the "red" bees all performed the tail-wagging dance. In the round dance, the dancing bees run in circles. In the tail-wagging dance they run in a straight line wagging their abdomen to and fro, then return to the starting point in a semicircle, repeat the tail-wagging run, return in a semicircle on the other side, and so on (Fig. 29).

I knew this wagging dance well, and had described it 20 years earlier as the dance of the pollen-collecting bees. Now it turned out that I had been mistaken. The round dance signified a food source that was close at hand, the wagging dance one that was 50–100 yards away or more. The error arose from the fact that I had always placed my dishes with sugar water close to the hive and that therefore the only wagging dances I had observed were those of pollen-gatherers returning from their natural collection sites farther away.

This surprising observation was soon followed by another: if our feeding site was some 100 yards to the west of the hive and we placed observation dishes with the same characteristic scent, one to the east, the other to the west, at similar distances from the hive, many new foragers would turn up in the west, but hardly any in the east. If on the following day we switched the food dish to the east, the main stream of foragers would turn east and the bees would lose their interest in westward flight. Did the bees also possess a signal to indicate direction?

This seemed altogether too fantastic to be true, and on thinking the matter over, my joy of discovery became rather deflated. For there was a much more probable explanation: namely, that the olfactory attractant, which bees produce in their scent organs and which they are in the habit of releasing when approaching a food source as a guide to searching newcomers, is discernible over much greater distances than had previously been assumed and that it was

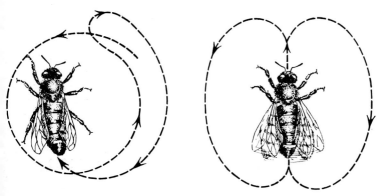

FIG. 29.   The bees' track during the round dance (*left*) and the tail-wagging dance (*right*).

this scent which accounted for the newcomers and not a direction signal.

To clear up this point, we established our feeding station on a spot where no foraging bees could be expected to appear unless they were especially directed, that is, on a narrow, stony footpath that ran between the lake on one side and forest and rock on the other, a good few hundred yards away from the hive. A few minutes after the bees had been offered concentrated sugar water in place of the weak solution they had been fed before, and had started to dance accordingly, whole hosts of newcomers came swarming to this secluded spot. My immediate reaction to this sight was one of instinctive recoil—I did not want to believe what I could see with my own eyes. But the facts were indisputable.

There was just one more alternative hypothesis. Could it not be that the foragers exposed their scent glands while flying from the hive to the feeding place, thus marking an aerial trail for the novices to follow? Such a trail would, of course, not function for long if there was a wind. But rather than ponder about probabilities I wanted to be sure. It is not difficult to seal the bees' scent organ and this does not affect their dancing. Yet even after I had thus excluded the possibility of a scent-marked trail, the fellow foragers of the scentless bees found the remote feeding place as rapidly as before. The only explanation that fitted the observed facts was the assumption that the bees were somehow able to tell each other the direction of their target. At this point we had to break off our experiments because of the onset of winter.

The communication of distance was another unexplained mystery. The difference between round dance and tail-wagging dance alone did not suffice to explain this phenomenon, for the tail-wagging type began to be used for food sources 50–100 yards distant from the hive, but equally reliably and swiftly directed foraging bees to food sources situated at distances of 1000 yards or more.

During the winter there was nothing we could do but wait, though this inactivity was difficult to bear. With the first warm days of spring 1945 we took up the matter anew.

Careful observation enabled us to solve these mysteries: when we compared the wagging dances of bees that had been feeding at carefully arranged distances we noticed a difference in rhythm. When the food source is 100 yards away, the dance is so fast that the straight run is performed 9–10 times in 15 seconds. With increasing distance the speed of the dances decreases systematically. To each distance there corresponds a definite speed. It is remarkable that this ritual has international validity. American bees can understand European bees without difficulty. And M. Lindauer, who engaged in what might be called "comparative philology" of the bees' language, found the same method of indicating distance in different species of social bees in India (the only country where there are more than one species whose social organization resembles that of our honey-bees) though the rhythmic pattern of their dance is slightly different.

The solution we found for the bees' method of indicating direction was, if anything, even more remarkable. I remember the hour: it was midday on 15 June 1945 when I realized that all marked dancers which had collected their sugar water at a feeding place about 400 yards due north of the hive performed their wagging run straight down on the vertical honeycomb, whereas unmarked bees which were collecting at other, unknown sites danced in all possible directions. During the hours that followed my marked group gradually changed the direction of the run counter-clockwise by the same angle by which in the meantime the sun had moved clockwise across the sky. When I arranged a second feeding place in the opposite direction to the first, and fed both groups simultaneously, one group would perform their tail-wagging run head down, and the other head up.

I realized then that the bees were able to indicate the actual direction of a food source by the choice of direction for their tail-wagging run, a choice which was influenced by the position of the sun. In the darkness of the hive, the angle of the sun that had to be kept when flying to the distant goal was symbolized in their dances on the vertical honeycomb by a corresponding angle to the force of gravity as follows: a tail-wagging run straight up meant that the food source lay in the direction of the sun. A run deviating by a given angle to the left or right from the "up" direction indicated a direction of flight deviating by the same angle from the position of the sun to the left or right (Fig. 30).

Against all expectation and probability, the original, seemingly far-fetched hypothesis had turned out to be correct after all. The bees were really able to impart to their fellow workers the exact location, by distance and direction, of a given source of food miles away from the hive. An enormous number of experiments which I have not touched upon here had to be made, however, and every conceivable method of testing and counter-testing had to be applied before the facts could be stated with absolute certainty.

In the same year I received an invitation to lecture in Zürich, which provided my first opportunity to talk about these discoveries to a larger audience. I enjoyed tremendously my visit to a country

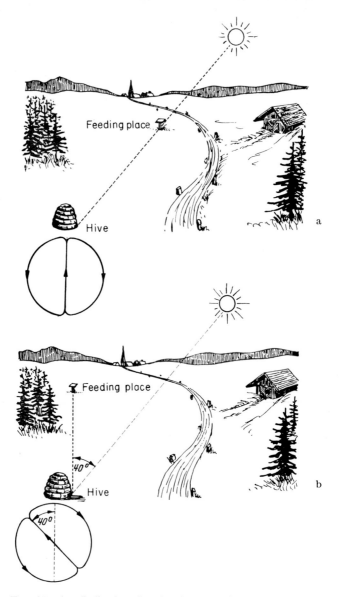

FIG. 30a, b. Indicating direction by the tail-wagging dance. On the vertical honeycomb (a) a tail-wagging run straight up, signifying a goal in the direction of the sun; (b) a tail-wagging run at an angle of 40 degrees to the left (counted from an upward run) a goal of 40 degrees to the left of the sun, etc. (Enlarged diagrams of the runs below the hives.)

unscathed by the horrors of war where one could get anything the heart desired, and delighted in the keen interest of an audience able to listen with an undivided mind. After years of isolation and vexation, this atmosphere of freedom acted like a balm to my bruised spirits. I have often been to Switzerland but never, before or after, did I feel with such gratitude the rugged strength of this small nation that had stood like a rock against the onslaught of evil forces.

GRAZ, 1946–1950

IN THE year 1946 I was asked whether I would like to take over the vacant chair of zoology in Graz and become a professor in my native country. Several factors influenced my decision: one was that conditions in Munich were appalling. I was convinced that the Institute could not possibly become functional again before it was time for me to retire (I was then 60 years old). Our house was a heap of rubble, and the mere thought of Munich evoked in me painful memories of the events of the last decade. A change of environment, I thought, might help to restore that peace of mind without which no fruitful scientific work is possible.

Graz is a beautiful city, nestling pleasantly in the foothills of the Styrian Alps, and has a mild climate favouring interesting southern forms of plant and animal life. It had suffered comparatively little from the war. Its university had a glorious tradition, but two ruthless purges, one by the Nazis in 1938, and another—after their overthrow—against their nominees had so depleted the ranks of the teaching staff that the very continuance of this seat of learning seemed in danger. The Zoological Institute was spacious and well equipped. True, one corner had been destroyed by a direct hit, but what was that compared to Munich, where only one corner was usable—at a pinch. In Graz there were gaps in the rows of houses. In Munich, a few isolated buildings stood like islands in a sea of rubble.

In these circumstances I felt that I was justified in devoting my remaining energies to scientific research at Graz rather than to the rehabilitation of the Munich Institute, especially as this task was in the capable hands of one of my oldest friends and colleagues, Professor Ruth Beutler. An incurable optimist, she promised to look after things in Munich until they got back to normal and I should return. I myself was less sanguine and thought of my departure as

146

final. Yet she held on to her belief against all odds, and by sheer perseverance made it come true.

With prodigious energy she strove to put zoology on its feet again and valiantly defended the remnants of the Institute against encroachments from other departments that had fared even worse and cast covetous eyes in our direction. The chief danger came from the Department of Chemistry. I myself had offered Professor Wieland part of our building as a temporary refuge since it did not look as if we should need all of it in the foreseeable future. This arrangement had its initial advantages, for the chemists, who were on good terms with industry, managed in a surprisingly short time to have a new third storey and a new roof erected on the walls that were still standing. Thereafter the building could be re-equipped and refitted for use. Before long, however, what had seemed at first a mutually advantageous symbiosis developed into a serious threat. The chemists were expansionists and tried to get rid of us altogether, suggesting that we should join the botanists in far-off Nymphenburg. Thanks to Ruth Beutler's ceaseless defence of our rights, we managed to hold on to one half of the building while the chemists occupied the other half. In this struggle she was ably assisted by Professor W. Jacobs, the successor of Holtfreter in the post of Conservator, to whom I also wish to pay tribute for his successful efforts to get normal zoology courses going again despite an almost complete lack of teaching aids. In fact, we would have needed the whole building much sooner than any one had expected; but it took quite 10 years before we saw the last of the chemists.

At Graz the housing shortage was acute. For 2 years my wife and I had to make do with my room at the Institute, which served in turn as office, study, bedroom, sitting room, bathroom, and kitchen (not that there was much to cook in those days). I suppose it was only natural that my wife and I did not always see eye to eye on the crucial problem of change-over from official to domestic function.

One thing was hard: we were cut off from our children, who had all stayed on the other side of the frontier between Germany and Austria which was still hermetically closed. When we were in Brunnwinkl for the summer, they naturally wanted to come, and as permits were not obtainable, they tried to cross illegally. Quite often they succeeded. Once, a kind American officer brought Otto to us as "his prisoner", and took him back again to Munich at the end of vacation. Sometimes their luck did not hold. For instance, when Leni, sitting by the stream which separated the two countries, was asked what she was doing there. "I am having breakfast" was her reply. But since she could not really explain why she had to take off her shoes and stockings for the purpose, she had to follow the guard and submit to hours of interrogation at the frontier post. When the officer released her in the evening, not without having imposed a stiff fine, he mentioned casually that at this time of the day there were no patrols. . . .

Gradually, however, things became easier and, when at last we had moved to a pleasant flat in Theodor-Körner-Strasse, we were joined by Otto, who had successfully graduated from school and taken up zoology at Graz University.

My inaugural lecture was on the subject "Medical training and the study of biology". My choice was dictated by a recent decision of the Austrian Ministry of Education to abolish biology as a compulsory examination subject for students of medicine. Admittedly, biology remained in the curriculum, but it is a truism that the majority of students can only be made to occupy themselves with any academic subject by the fear of being ploughed in examinations. Hence dropping the examination was to all intents and purposes tantamount to dropping the subject.

This action was in line with a trend by no means confined to Austria. It was but a general consequence of the rapidly increasing load of subject matter to be mastered. Since there is a limit to what the human brain can absorb and retain, students had to be relieved of some less important matters, of which, in the view of the authorities, biology was one.

But their decision showed that they did not sufficiently appreciate how intimately this subject is connected with the study of *Man*, whose life and health will be the chief concern of the young doctor. The human body obeys the same fundamental natural laws as the rest of the animal kingdom. Practically without exception these laws were first discovered in animals and can best be taught on their bodies. Many facts are much easier to observe and to understand in lower animals than in the highly complex human body. At a time when it is at last generally recognized that excessive specialization is harmful and that the doctor must always treat the whole patient and not only any one diseased organ, the study of the fundamental laws of life and a thorough understanding of the functioning of the human body, such as can only be gained by comparison with other living organisms, are absolutely indispensable for medical knowledge and skill.

All this I tried to explain in my inaugural. The matter was, and is, very near to my heart: for in my long life as a teacher I enjoyed nothing more than the task of introducing medical students to the problems of general biology and the comparative anatomy of vertebrates—possibly because I felt myself closely linked to the medical profession by family tradition, early training, and personal experience during the First World War.

To this day medical students in Austria are not obliged to pass an examination in biology. The fact that an increasing number sit for it voluntarily shows that they have a better understanding of priorities than the official bodies concerned.

The Graz Institute was reasonably well equipped for teaching, but the scarcity of funds for equipment greatly impeded research until, for the second time in my life, I received succour from the Rockefeller Foundation. In 1949 they granted us a considerable sum for our research plans and supported them, not only during this period of exceptional stringency, but even later when I had returned to Munich. I greatly appreciated the way they produced a maximum of scientific effect with a minimum of red tape.

In addition the Foundation made a special grant to Graz University for the restoration of the zoology building. When the bomb damage had been made good, the Institute was richer by a beautiful new lecture hall.

During those years at Graz the main direction of my research work had been determined by a chance observation at Brunnwinkl. It took us from the internal problem of communication within the hive to the problem of orientation in the field, where psychological performance and the physiology of the senses are inextricably interlocked, and the former cannot be understood without an understanding of the latter. The language of the bees turned out to be far more complex than we had thought in the beginning. In the general analysis of our findings it was often necessary to base one conclusion upon another. An edifice of this sort becomes a little precarious unless the foundations are on really firm ground, and for this reason even matters that seemed to be 100 per cent certain were put to the test. One of these was the assumption, which indeed it seemed not possible to doubt, that the bees' dances in ordinary hives were exactly the same as those in our observation hive. Nevertheless, I wanted to make sure. I therefore opened such an ordinary hive, lifted out a honeycomb or two and saw to my satisfaction that the marked bees, for which feeding places had been arranged at a given distance and direction, danced in exactly the same manner as in our observation hive. So far, so good. Following a sudden impulse of curiosity, I turned one of the honeycombs covered with dancing bees in my hand so that I now held it horizontally. I wanted to find out how the bees would cope with a situation in which they were unable to translate the angle between the directions of feeding place and sun to an angle between the direction of their run and the force of gravity. But instead of the confusion I had expected I found that the bees continued their wagging dances as if the sudden change from the vertical to the horizontal was all in the day's work for them, except that now their wagging runs were pointing straight to the feeding place just as we point to a distant goal with raised arm and outstretched finger. When I turned the honeycomb round and round in the horizontal plane like a turntable the bees were in no way put out, but adjusted to the right direction like the needle of a compass.

   It took me quite a time to find the very simple explanation for this surprising phenomenon, but there is no need to withhold it from the reader. When the forager flies to the feeding place, she notes the direction of the sun and remembers the angle between her line of flight and the position of the sun. This is the angle she normally translates to an angle with the perpendicular line of gravity when dancing on a vertical surface (p. 143). But when she dances on a horizontal surface in the open, there is no need for such a translation. She places herself in the wagging run in such a way that she sees the sun in the same direction and at the same angle as during the actual flight, and that means, of course, that she points straight to the source (Fig. 31). In this way the novices following her learn immediately the position they have to adopt in respect to the sun in their flight towards the goal. The situation is not quite so strange to the bees as it would seem, for during warm weather quite a number of bees sometimes gather on the horizontal landing board in front of the flight hole, and under these circumstances one can observe the returning foragers dancing horizontally.

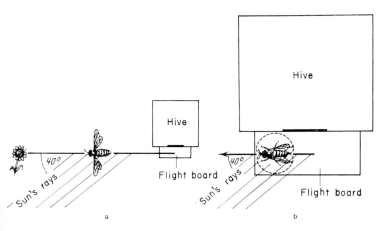

FIG. 31a, b. Indicating direction by reference to the sun's position when dancing on a horizontal surface. (a) Line of flight from hive to feeding place; (b) wagging dance on horizontal surface.

There was a reason for my slowness in discovering this apparently simple explanation. Because I wanted to study this novel form of direction-indicating without disturbance, I laid my observation hive flat so that the honeycombs were horizontal and arranged a wooden roof above it for protection against the weather, especially against any overheating of the honeycombs under the glass front (now uppermost) by direct insolation. The dancers were therefore in the shade, but, though they could not see the sun, they pointed correctly to the target.

At first I thought they were guided by terrestrial magnetism. This turned out to be incorrect, for magnetic forces did not disturb them at all. Then it occurred to me that they might be sensitive to penetrating long wave rays and could sense the sun through the wooden roof. This hypothesis collapsed when I surrounded my horizontal hive with walls on all sides so that the dancers could not see the sky at all. That caused complete bewilderment, and the dancers danced all anyhow, without orientation of any kind. But as soon as they were shown even a tiny circle of blue sky through a stove pipe inserted in one wall, their dances immediately assumed the right direction. When, with the help of a mirror, I showed them the image of the southern sky through an opening pointing due north, they indicated the direction in reverse, looking-glass fashion. This fact strongly suggested that the bees were able to perceive in the blue sky a something or other which depended on the position of the sun, and which made it possible for them to orient themselves by reference to the sun without actually seeing it.

When I discussed the matter with H. Benndorf, our Professor of Physics at Graz, and with Professor O. Kiepenheuer at Freiburg, a specialist in celestial phenomena, they both suggested that the polarized light emitted by the sky might somehow be involved. The light emanating from a clear sky is largely polarized, that is to say, the light waves vibrate in one plane only, and the direction of this plane is at every point determined by the position of the sun at a given moment. If the eyes of the bees should be capable of perceiving the plane of vibration of polarized light, their behaviour would be understandable. But nobody knew anything about that, and on the whole the theory seemed so unlikely that very strong evidence would be needed to accept it.

To test this hypothesis a large polaroid (a material which causes transmitted light to vibrate in one direction only) would be required, but such a thing was not available in Austria. When, however, my friend August Krogh from Copenhagen, with whom I had corresponded about the matter, happened to be in America, he sent me a polaroid measuring 6 by 12 in., of a kind used over there as an anti-dazzle device. I placed it above a horizontal honeycomb covered with dancing bees. I cannot begin to describe the blissful sensation of tension relieved which I experienced when

I observed how the bees responded to the horizontal rotations I imparted to the foil and adjusted their dances to the changes this caused in the plane of vibration of the light reflected from the sky. Here, then, was definite proof that the bees were able to analyse polarized light and could use its plane of vibration as a means of orientation. Naturally, many more experiments than I can describe here were needed to check and support this conclusion.

I vividly recall how one day when I was still at university the talk around the family table turned to some rather extraordinary scientific discoveries; and I can still hear the deep bass of my uncle Sigmund Exner remarking in his driest manner: "The explanation of most such extraordinary facts is simply that they are not true."

This aptly summed up the attitude of a great many biologists to my latest discoveries about the language of the bees. One man declared straight out that he did not propose to believe this sort of thing. Another—it was Professor Thorpe from Cambridge—made the journey from England to Brunnwinkl to see for himself. My demonstrations and his own experiments convinced him that the bees did in fact possess these faculties with which nobody really wanted to credit them.

I always carry a notebook (a must for people with a poor memory) in which several pages are devoted to bees' projects and there I jot down all the experiments which I mean to carry out. The summer is not always long enough to get through the whole programme, and quite often some tests have to be postponed to the next season. One experiment had suffered this fate repeatedly: I had planned to feed a group of marked bees somewhere a few hundred yards from the hive, and then to transport the whole hive to a distant place. I wanted to find out whether even in strange surroundings the bees would search for the food to which they were accustomed in the same direction and at the same distance. Although I vaguely expected this to happen I told myself that in all probability the thing would not work and this was the reason why this rather complicated experiment was put back so often. However, on the morning of 24 September 1949 we did eventually take our observation hive by boat many miles across the lake. It contained a group of thirty bees, all individually numbered, that had been fed for several days about 200 yards to the west of the hive (Fig. 32a). After the hive had been put down in the middle of extensive featureless meadows we placed food tables 200 yards to the east, west, north, and south; each was manned by an observer, I myself taking the western table, prepared for a long

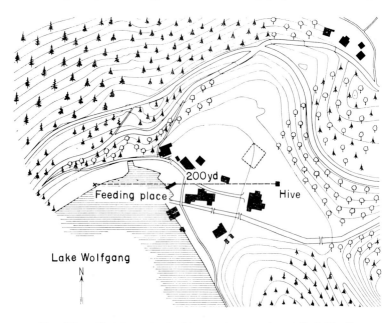

FIG. 32a.   Sketchmap to the hive-moving experiment. Individually numbered bees are trained at Brunnwinkl to a feeding site 200 yards to the west of the hive.

fruitless wait (Fig. 32b). But only a few minutes after the flight hole had been uncovered, the first numbered bee came buzzing along. As soon as she alighted she had to be caught, for otherwise she would have alerted the others. As the bees arrived in quick succession I had some highly exciting sport, and only my helpers in the other directions had to suffer boredom. Again the hardly credible had become a fact.

We have repeated this type of experiment a great many times with various modifications. The results can be stated in a few words. Bees use for their orientation in the field not only certain salient landmarks which they have observed, but likewise the sun

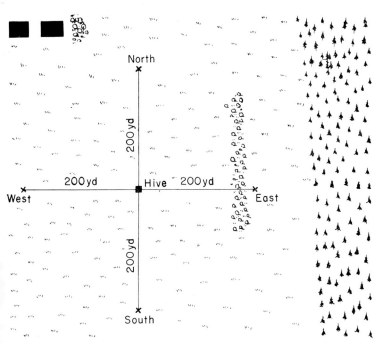

FIG. 32b. Transported to a strange site in a completely different landscape, the bees search again 200 yards west of the hive and ignore the feeding tables placed in the three other directions of the compass.

as compass. Although the sun changes its position in the sky from sunrise to sunset, the bees are capable of finding a direction in which they are interested at any time of the day. Two things are necessary for this feat: they must know the exact time and they must know the position of the sun at any given moment. Thanks to a very accurate internal clock (cf. pp. 177–178) and a knowledge of the sun's daily movements based on experience, these conditions are fulfilled. That much we can ascertain through our experiments. But about the nature of their psychological sensations which so unerringly guide their winged flight the bees, alas, cannot tell us anything.

If we add to these achievements the fact that bees can perceive the sun through cloud and that they can deduce its position with the help of polarized light from the sky, the truly miraculous nature of the bee-eye as an instrument of navigation becomes apparent. Any patch of blue sky, however small, can aid their orientation. It is not for nothing that their compound eyes are enormous structures taking in the whole sky and the whole earth at one glance. A thousand minute individual eyes anchor a flying bee to the celestial compass. Compared to such optical equipment, which would be the envy of any seafaring man, the performance of our own organs of sight seems distinctly poor.

I ought to mention here that these remarkable feats are not confined to the bees. Other insects, crustaceans, and spiders have also been found to possess the capacity for analysing polarized light, and it looks as if the ability to use the celestial compass with due consideration of the time of day is also a widespread accomplishment among arthropods.

SECOND JOURNEY TO THE STATES,
1949

REMEMBERING my friends' cheery "Come over again", I accepted with alacrity when Professor D. R. Griffin of Cornell University, Ithaca, N.Y., invited me to give a few talks on my bees. He was sure further lectures at other universities would follow. After years of isolation the chance of seeing something of scientific progress in a country which had forged ahead with giant strides was an exciting prospect.

When I returned from my first American trip on the S.S. *Bremen*, the catapulting of a mail-carrying aircraft from her deck as she neared land had been a sensational innovation. But by now airmail and air travel had become commonplace. Since flying saved time and my wife, who accompanied me this time, does not like sea voyages as much as I do, we, too, decided to fly. True, we were both a little nervous; we had never flown before and did not know how we should feel. In the event we both liked this mode of conveyance. Personally, however, I still find a sea voyage far more enjoyable.

On 11 March 1949 an uneventful train journey took us from Graz to Vienna, but the next day we had a double dose of the excitement of modern travel. When we got to Tulln Airport for the start of our flight to London, where we were to begin our transatlantic flight, a southeastern gale enveloped the whole airfield in black clouds of dust. While we were waiting to be called to the plane we heard somebody remark about our pilot: "If he tries to take off today his crate will be upside-down in no time." Fortunately, he did not try. We had to wait till next day, but then all went smoothly and on the morning of 14 March we duly landed at La Guardia Airport, New York. The following day we continued to Ithaca in a small plane which took us across lovely lake scenery in a full-scale blizzard. After a time the pilot remarked that "it

157

was a bit choppy". We had been aware of that fact unaided. However, he got us to our destination according to plan. The jaundice and flu, on the other hand, I caught immediately on arrival was not in the programme. I was compelled to cancel one of my lectures because I really was very poorly for a few days. But thanks to the latest achievements of American medical science and Dr. Griffin's devoted care, I was soon all right again.

For 2 months we travelled by train, aeroplane, and car across the whole vast continent as far as the Californian coast, but, partly no doubt because there was no need for me to inspect so many laboratories, the whole tour was not such a mad rush as the first one had been, and there was even a week of rest scheduled for the Easter recess.

We started off by revisiting Yale at New Haven, where we enjoyed meeting once more our old friend, Professor R. G. Harrison. But, alas, at Albertus Magnus College Mrs. Boveri was no longer present. She lay seriously ill in a nursing home near Princeton, where we were later able to see her for a short while.

Our journey was really a renewal of old friendships all the way. At Cambridge we were met by G. H. Parker who, though retired, was still immensely active. With justifiable pride he showed us over the new building of the Biological Institute which, like the old one, housed the representatives of animal and plant sciences under one spacious roof. As a German biologist I felt somewhat stunned when I was told that there were 15 professors of zoology, 14 of botany, and 50 assistants. Of the many interesting exhibits I particularly remember those of C. Williams. He had inserted transparent little "windows" into pupae of some lepidoptera, through which you could see their hearts pulsate, and, if you had patience, watch them turn into butterflies. He had also operatively joined about a dozen pupae end to end into a sort of chain. Because he had removed a small organ producing a substance which triggers off metamorphosis, he could keep them in the pupal stage as long as he wished. But if he implanted the organ secreting this hormone at one end of the chain, the whole series was soon transformed into a garland of butterflies. A layman may look at such things as no more than amusing stunts. But the expert is impressed by the originality of methods which have actually led to important discoveries.

The biological laboratories at Harvard are among the most beautiful I have ever seen. It is well known that some of the private universities, founded on rich donations and lovingly supported by grateful alumni, outshine their counterparts relying on public funds.

At a dinner in New Haven we met F. Osborn, the director of the New York Zoological Gardens, who invited us to visit his establishment when we should be in New York. At the luncheon party preceding that visit I sat next to W. Beebe, well known for having been the first man to descend to a depth of 1000 yards in his famous diving bell because he wanted to see for himself what life was like near the bottom of the deep sea. The richness of the fauna he found there and the pyrotechnics of luminous organs encountered in what had been thought of as the dark and silent deep astounded not only himself but the whole world of biologists. At 71, Beebe was still full of new plans. He had just discovered a marvellous place for a jungle laboratory in the tropical forest of Trinidad. When we met him again, 2 months later, he had already collected the considerable funds necessary to realize his plan and it did not take long before some very interesting papers from his own pen and those of his fellow workers came out of this institute.

New York Zoo is so vast that we were glad of the car that was put at our disposal. Among the exhibits I especially remember some rare specimens of billed platypus. These almost mythical egg-laying mammals from Australia were kept in strict seclusion as it was hoped that they might breed if they were not disturbed. I was also impressed by the colourful spectacle of humming birds, of which a dozen different species were kept in separate glass-fronted aviaries. But I did not enjoy them so much in captivity as when I saw them later flitting about collecting nectar from tropical flowers that matched their plumage in colourful splendour.

In certain ways I found the New York Museum of Natural History even more impressive than the Zoo. Never before had I seen such marvellously life-like exhibits so beautifully and lavishly arranged. Where in other collections you might see one stuffed elephant, or perhaps an adult with young, here in Africa Hall you could admire a whole herd of 9 to 10 beautiful specimens, each in itself a work of art, most beautifully displayed. Around the walls there were elaborate panoramas: for instance, a group of gorillas in which every stone, every blade of grass in the foreground belongs genuinely to their habitat and blends imperceptibly into a skilfully painted illusionist background. Or an ostrich's nest in the sand, complete with eggs and newly hatched chicks, the parents shown in defensive positions against a group of wart hogs depicted as they hesitate to drive home their attack. Words cannot hope to describe such artistry of representation.

On 8 April I had lunch with W. Weaver, the Director of the Rockefeller Foundation and half a dozen senior members of his staff on the 55th floor of an imposing building. As they all seemed to have the cause of goodwill and understanding between nations very much at heart, I talked to them, at Weaver's request, about communication among bees. For in certain respects the bees' organization and mutual collaboration even in artificially mixed communities is indeed superior to our own efforts. Later Weaver and I had a private chat about old times, the fate of our Institute, my present position at Graz, and my plans for the future. As a result of this conversation I received the grant towards my research projects which has been mentioned earlier.

Our next stop was Princeton, where during my lecture I suddenly noticed the striking features of Albert Einstein among my hearers. In my opinion the presence of an exceptionally intelligent face in the audience will always be a spur to a lecturer. It puts him on his mettle. But I like also to watch a really stupid person when I give a popular talk. If I can detect a flicker of understanding on such a countenance I am satisfied that I am doing all right. Einstein invited us to visit him in his laboratory the following day, and we had a lively discussion with this wise and humorous man. I remembered vividly how 40 years earlier my uncle Franz Exner, the physicist, had tried to give some idea of Einstein's brilliant achievement, then quite new, to our little circle of hopelessly ignorant laymen.

From Princeton we went on to Washington, the last stage of the first half of my lecture tour. Our considerate hosts had planned that we should spend a week of rest and relaxation during the Easter recess at the Laboratory for Primate Behaviour in Florida. The station, which was attached to Yale, had been founded by Professor R. M. Yerkes whom I had had the pleasure of meeting in 1930. Now his successor, Professor K. S. Lashley, met us at Jacksonville Airport and took us in his car to Orange Park where the station is situated. Alas, the groves that had given the place its name had been killed by a frost some 50 years ago and had never been replaced.

We were shown to our flat on the first floor of one of the staff houses in the grounds. There we found an icebox thoughtfully stocked with every conceivable kind of food hygienically packed and ready for consumption. We were to feel free to relax in complete privacy if we wished though, needless to say, we were often invited and generally looked after in the friendliest manner by our hosts.

Not that there was much peace and quiet to enjoy during the first night of our stay! Our neighbours, the chimpanzees in some open-air enclosures near by, never stopped making an unearthly row all night, and when we visited them in the morning, they were still in a state of great excitement. A little baby chimp had been born during the night, and this had upset the whole community.

When we saw it, it had a white nappy on, like all other chimpanzee babies there. It had been taken away from its mother and handed to a nurse for purposes of research.

This was not infrequently done. In the house of Dr. Hayes and his wife, both on the staff of the station, we met Vicky, then 18 months old, who had been adopted by the childless couple at birth and brought up like a human baby. The idea was to find out how far chimpanzees could be made to develop mentally. The foster parents hoped she would learn to speak. But in this they were doomed to disappointment. Vicky learned to say "Mummy" but all efforts to teach her other words failed. In her behaviour she closely resembled a naughty baby girl. She pulled my wife's shoes off her feet and threw them into the furthermost corner of the room, and was full of such naughty tricks, enjoying most what was most strongly forbidden.

The adult chimpanzees in the open-air enclosures were not free of bad habits either. They loved bombarding passing visitors with handfuls of dust and gravel, or to spit at them, carefully filling their mouths with water beforehand as they apparently did not think their spit went far enough. Although we had been warned, my wife received a direct hit smack in the face.

Yerkes had chosen this site for the station because it combined comparative nearness to Yale with a climate suitable for primates. It is even claimed that their health is better there than in their native habitats. Hence it is possible to engage in psychological, anatomical and evolutionary studies of these our closest relatives without the trouble and expense of a safari in tropical countries.

On our walks in the countryside around the station we found a great deal to interest us. The whole landscape receives its characteristic stamp from a greyish-green growth hanging from trees rather like tattered shrouds (Fig. 33) which is called Spanish moss. It is, however, neither Spanish, nor a moss, but a member of the family of Bromeliaceae, related to pineapple, with the scientific name of *Tillandsia usneoides*. Though not strictly a parasite, it slowly kills the trees it grows on by suffocation.

On the sandy banks of St. John's River we enjoyed watching a large colony of fiddler crabs. The behaviour of these curious creatures in which one claw grows to the size of their bodies while the other remains quite small has often been described. They are really too funny for words as they sit in front of their burrows weaving their white claws about like fiddle bows in measured rhythms in order to emphasize their rights of territory and, we must presume, to impress their ladies.

Another time we walked along a road passing through sandy country sparsely covered with vegetation. At our approach innumerable grasshoppers (I found out later that their Latin name is *Scistetica marmorata*) rose into the air. A curious flight habit enabled them to make particularly effective use of their virtually perfect protective colouring. They flew in zigzag line, and by changing direction at an acute angle immediately before alighting they came down in an unexpected spot and disappeared as if by magic. Our observations were constantly interrupted by well-meaning motorists offering us lifts. On the whole we managed, though occasionally with some difficulty, to explain to these friendly people what we were doing. But when we started to walk home along the road to get a bit of exercise, people thought we must be completely crazy, and in the end we had to give in and get into a car.

The most interesting excursion of all took us by car southwards to Marineland; there, on a sparsely inhabited stretch of coast

FIG. 33.   By St. John's River: "Spanish moss".

but within easy reach of a lively motor road, the Oceanarium, the greatest aquarium of the world, is open to the public. In two enormous concrete basins we saw adult dolphins, those master swimmers of the oceans, sharks, turtles, and hosts of other marine animals. From a dark passage which led around the basins below surface level it was possible to watch all these creatures through glass windows as they disported themselves under water. The dolphins, however, were at their most exciting when they leaped high into the air, exposing the whole of their beautiful, streamlined bodies in order to take some fish out of the hand of their keeper who stood on a platform high above the water (Fig. 34). Immediately behind me there was the open sea, where their brothers disported themselves happily close to the shore in blessed freedom.

FIG. 34. Dolphins leaping to take their dinner from their keeper's hand. Oceanarium, Marineland, Florida. (*Photograph Marine Studios, Marineland, Florida, U.S.A.*)

The Oceanarium had at that time been in existence for about 10 years. It was beginning to pay its way, but its use for research had only just begun.

Our week's holiday was over all too quickly. The second part of my lecture tour took us via Columbus and Ann Arbor to Chicago, where we experienced the hottest 3rd May recorded in the city but, nevertheless, enjoyed a pleasant day in the company of Paul Weiss, the biologist, A. E. Emerson, the termite specialist, and other interesting people. Emerson had just brought back from a journey to the Belgian Congo a sizable collection of termite mounds. Some of these impressed me greatly. For these minute builders in their thousands have no means of viewing as a whole the outcome of their joint collaboration, and yet the finished structures look as if they had been planned by some thinking architect.

I admired equally some of the ingenious ideas of American builders. Whenever I think of Chicago, I recall the magnificent motorway along Lake Michigan which links it to its own sprawling suburbs. Normally, the eight lanes of this road are divided into four in each direction by a low wall in the middle. But in the evening rush hour, when most of the traffic is away from the city, the middle wall disappears, and a similar one rises two lanes farther left, dividing the road into six "out" and two "in" lanes. In the morning it is the other way round.

We went along this magnificent road when A. B. Hasler called for us in his car to take us to Madison for my next lecture, at the University of Wisconsin. I could not describe the beautiful scenery we passed on this journey even if I wanted to. But I want to mention a little incident which seemed to be characteristic of the country. At a farm belonging to a friend of Hasler's we watched an inventory being taken of the fish in a trout stream, reach by reach. After the fish had been stunned with electrical implements they were caught and weighed, and quickly released again. To my surprise I learned from the owner that he himself was not interested in fishing. But the farm specialized in milk treated in various ways for digestive complaints by reducing fat or protein content, etc. The trout stream was intended to provide sport for the doctors on whose prescriptions the farmer depended for his profits. And he wanted to be able to send his best customers to the reaches with the largest fish. The medical specialization of the farm was reflected in its exceptional cleanliness. The cows were actually habit-trained. An electrified yoke made them take a step back every time they relieved themselves, causing the dung to fall in a flushed channel running along their stalls. Apparently they quickly learn to do this automatically without further need for the electric shock, and in this way their floor is kept perfectly clean.

Near Princeton we were shown another instance of the latest dairying methods testifying to the importance accorded to scrupulous hygiene. It was a "rotolactor", an enormous turntable on which 1550 cows were being milked electrically three times a day, day in and day out, 30 at a time, conveyor-belt fashion. The whole business from the cleaning of udders with jets of water and their drying with warm towels and hot air to the weighing and disposal of the milk, carried out, needless to say, by men in spotless white overalls, took about 10 min, the time required for the turntable to complete one revolution.

We spent some pleasant and instructive days at Madison which, through its position in the midst of four lakes, surely must be one of the most beautifully situated university towns in the world. Hasler, who worked on the biology of fisheries and the physiology of fish, showed us a sub-station of his institute built right on the banks of Lake Mendota, where the fish, one might say, come swimming straight into the zoologist's laboratory.

From Madison, Hasler's car took us a considerable distance to Minneapolis, where we were once more the guests of D. E. Minnich. In 1930 this had been the westernmost point of my journey. This time we were to go on. But before we started on the great leap to the Californian coast we made a detour to Iowa. My former fellow student Witschi, who had been my host on that first trip, happened to be in Europe for a year and his place was taken temporarily by the Swiss zoologist F. Baltzer from Berne. He and his wife lived in Witschi's house and we spent a most enjoyable evening with our old friends—something we had not done for years when we lived in neighbouring countries. While we sat in the garden after dark, the American fire-flies gave us a magnificent display. Hundreds of them were flying about close to the ground. They did not glow continuously as ours do, but in short brilliant bursts at regular intervals, say once a second. The rhythm of glowing differs between species and serves as an identification signal. The female glowworms, waiting in the grass, respond to the right rhythm by glowing back in the same intervals. Nature has never been at a loss for novel ways of starting love affairs between her creatures.

When we arrived the following evening above San Francisco

after an exciting flight across the Rockies and the Utah desert, the scintillation of the city's innumerable coloured lights presented an equally fantastic spectacle. Between the lights the bay itself lay in pitch darkness except for the luminous line marking the 6-mile bridge that cut right across its black expanse. In day-time, this bridge turned out to be an impressive but rather ugly piece of engineering. Yet its twin, spanning the entry to the bay at the Golden Gate, proved clearly that a bridge of many miles could also be a breathtaking work of art.

The luscious tins of Californian pears, peaches, and other delicious kinds of fruit which we were wont to enjoy at home had made me expect to find a flowering orchard of a country, and I had looked forward to bathing in the warm waters of the Pacific. I found that I had to readjust my ideas quite a bit. True, in San Francisco and in the neighbouring Berkeley where we were staying there were enchanting gardens glowing with roses and colourful carpets of mesembryanthemum. But we were not prepared for the expanse of barren soil outside the cities, interrupted only farther inland by irrigated fertile plantations, nor for the cold currents and frequent fogs of the Pacific coast, which made us forget quickly enough about swimming.

We spent a good deal of time with Richard Goldschmidt, who was now teaching at the University of California in Berkeley. Forty years ago he had taught me to study the smallest organisms through a microscope. Now he took us to some of the largest living things, and some of the oldest, the mammoth trees of the nearby National Park. The tallest species, *Sequoia gigantea*, it is true, occurs only farther up the mountains of the Sierra, but the beautiful stand of *Sequoia sempervirens* (Californian Redwood) he showed us was quite impressive enough for me. These giants of the forest rise something like 300 ft into the air—as high as the towers of the Frauenkirche at Munich.

On our return from this excursion we passed across the famous bridge of the Golden Gate and drove along a rocky coast to a beautiful, luxurious road house. Only some 200 yards away we watched a herd of sea lions basking on rocky cliffs close to the shore. The wind brought us their roar, and their stench, but the animals—they are, of course, protected—took no notice of the

M

bustle of modern civilization on their doorstep—another of these contrasts which strike a European as typical.

On our way south we stopped at Pacific Grove, an isolated research station of marine biology in beautiful surroundings near the little fishing town of Monterey, and there we had another opportunity of seeing wild seals and sea lions.

Our next stop was Los Angeles where I visited the California Institute of Technology, which, notwithstanding the original intention of its founder expressed in its name, had developed into an internationally famous centre of the biological sciences. It owed this distinction to the great geneticist Th. H. Morgan, whom I had had the privilege of meeting during my first visit. Although he had now been dead for 4 years, his spirit lived on in his institution. And it is perhaps characteristic of the man that this did not mean a slavish adherence to his methods. For instance, the tiny fruit fly *Drosophila,* which under Morgan had become almost synonymous with genetical research, was now in danger of being superseded by the mould fungus *Neurospora.* For unless techniques are continually adapted to new problems as they arise, and experimental organisms chosen accordingly, the fair plant of biological research cannot hope to thrive and bear fruit.

F. Went, a Dutchman who represented botany at the Institute, showed me the phytothron he had just finished building at a cost of 400,000 dollars. He was proud he had managed on so little. Perhaps this was really not much for such an accomplished research tool; it did indeed possess the most marvellous facilities for regulating the environment from temperature and humidity to artificial rain and wind.

On 30 May we flew from Los Angeles to New York, touching down only once, at Chicago. The flight (we spent 9 hours in the air) afforded us marvellous glimpses through the clouds on to sandy deserts with fantastic rock formations, the Grand Canyon, and range after range of snow-capped mountains in the Rockies, with pleasant human settlements nestling in the valleys amidst seas of yellow blossoms. Finally, before we landed in New York after nightfall, we watched the sun setting over Lake Erie in a blaze of glory.

Before returning to Europe we paid a brief farewell visit to

Griffin at Cornell University, who had originally suggested this trip, and there I talked for the last time to a group of practical beekeepers and scientific apiculturists. I had, of course, had many such meetings, and had often discussed the reasons for the higher honey yields in America—whether this was due to better natural conditions or to better and more efficient methods. There is a lot to be said for American practices, but even with the most sophisticated methods a German beekeeper is not likely to achieve a mean honey yield of 75 lb per hive which is quite common around Ithaca. Still, I do think that a study tour across the Atlantic would be most instructive for our beemasters. It is only to be hoped that they would not be disheartened by some of the techniques of large-scale operators: for instance, when they see the 1000-litre tanker used by one of them to pump the winter feed of sugar water to his many hives with a minimum of trouble in the shortest possible time.

On the morning of 8 June we flew non-stop from New York to London in 13 hours of uneventful flight. On 13 June it took us nearly as long to go from Munich to our home in Graz.

Both of my American tours, and a great many other journeys, I owe in the first place to the honey-bees. What these fascinating little insects have revealed to me about their lives has made me a welcome visitor in innumerable countries—Switzerland and Holland, Great Britain and France, Jugoslavia, Denmark, Sweden, Finland, and many others. If I had a gift for writing travellers' tales, I could go on for ever. For from each such journey I returned refreshed and mentally enriched. To my way of thinking there is no better way of gathering riches.

TO MUNICH FOR THE FIFTH TIME

DURING my stay in Austria the authorities in Munich had tried hard to find a successor for the chair I had vacated and had failed, several long-drawn-out negotiations having come to nothing. The conditions were really anything but attractive, and at the end of 4 years the vacancy had still not been filled. I therefore had to make up my mind whether or not I wanted to go back.

I was greatly attracted by the thought of rejoining the circle of old friends and former colleagues there, and also by the sizable group of gifted senior students who somehow had found their way to Munich. In Graz their number had remained disappointingly small. Yet without the aid of students working on their doctoral theses under me I could not hope to carry out those research projects for which the Rockefeller Foundation had given me financial backing and which eventually also received generous support from the Deutsche Forschungsgemeinschaft. What finally turned the scales was the fact that the Institute had been put back into working order far more quickly than I had thought possible. True it was not much to look at, and space was woefully tight. But the essentials for research and teaching were there.

I therefore accepted for the summer term of 1950. And so it came to pass that I returned to Munich to make my home there for the fifth time in my life.

True, as to "home", things were grim. Our house at Harlaching was the same sad heap of rubble as in 1944, with the difference that everything that was even remotely usable had been removed. The very flagstones of the pavement in front of our house had been carted away, and the garden was a wilderness. Weeds, alas, always grow so much more luxuriously than cultivated plants.

We were allotted a flat in a building in St. Paulsplatz which belonged to the university. Because it was largely inhabited by professors and such like, it was popularly known as the egghead barracks. We were not happy there. We felt hemmed in by houses on all sides, missed a garden, and disliked being so close to the Oktoberwiese, that famous fairground with its beer tents and noisy crowds in the autumn. How we longed for our own little place in Harlaching! Eventually, after some difficulties, we managed to get

FIG. 35. Our car, fully loaded. *In front:* my wife and myself; *second row:* Otto, to his left Maria, to his right Leni; *third row:* the grandchildren; behind them, Johanna Schreiner. Brunnwinkl, August 1951.

a smaller, more compact house built where the old one had been, and soon flowers grew around it as of old.

Occasionally it would really feel like old times when the whole family was gathered under our roof. But Hannerl has a family now herself and her own home at Tübingen. Maria is an assistant film producer whose work takes her away from home for long stretches at a time. But Leni, cruelly bereaved through the war, has returned to us and devotes her youthful energies partly to our home and partly to my work. Otto transferred his zoology studies from Graz to Munich and graduated there. Like myself, he had been fascinated by animals ever since he was a little boy. What he brought into the house in the way of birds and other animals far exceeded anything I myself had dared to inflict on my long-suffering family. At times our garden was a proper zoo, which was not always exactly good for the flowers. There was, for instance, a young roe deer Otto had raised on the bottle: it simply adored rosebuds. Otto later gave it to a wealthy landowner who became so fond of it that he had some roses planted especially for its delectation.

FIG. 36.   Rare friendship: fawn, tawny owl and bitch.

While it still ran about in our own garden, it loved playing with our dog, and with a young owl (Fig. 36). This was the most touching friendship among animals that I have ever encountered.

I must admit that I myself never quite ceased keeping pets too, but as time went on I became rather more selective. The small parrot Tschocki (cf. p. 17) had several successors of the same species which all inherited his name (its origin is shrouded in mystery). Four years ago we got yet another Tschocki, but this time it was a grey parrot from Australia. He actually looked like a small grey cockatoo with a saucy tuft of feathers on a yellow head and bright orange cheeks. This bird, which soon became the firm friend of all the family, is as different from my former green parakeets in behaviour as he is in plumage. Whereas they liked sweet things, as so many animals do, he definitely prefers savouries and helps himself to a few grains of pure salt at every meal. Though there is always plenty of food in his cage, he finds it much pleasanter to have his meals with us, sociable little creature that he is, and, besides, he prefers the variety of our table. Meal-times are the main events of the day for him, and should there be a delay for some reason he "creates" like anything. Unlike most parrots, he does not hold his food with his feet, but pulls whatever he fancies from the serving dish onto the table—say, spaghetti with tomato sauce. My wife was faced with the choice between constant family quarrels and a transparent nylon sheet to cover her linen table cloth. She chose the latter. Another peculiarity of our present Tschocki is that he never scratches his head as other members of the parrot family are wont to do, but demands this service from us. He often quite clearly asks me to join him in his cage for a pleasant chat, something none of his predecessors had ever expected of me. Unfortunately the door of the cage is only 4 by 4 in. Alas, so many things in life remain a dream!

I have not really acquired enough distance from these recent years to write about them in a mood of retrospective contemplation, yet before I close, I want to give some idea of the direction my scientific work took at that time.

All my activity was now concentrated on the honey-bees, for I was anxious to round off and complete the findings of the last 12 years' research on their communication and orientation. On this I worked in close collaboration with Dr. H. Heran, my assistant at Graz, and my Munich pupil Dr. M. Lindauer, who had also assisted me at Graz for a time. My chief concern was to discover, if possible, any further "words" in the bees' language. The bees, we knew, were able to tell their fellow workers exactly in what direction of the compass a given goal was to be found; could they also, if necessity arose, tell them to go "up" or "down"? To begin with, at Graz, the marked bees had to get used to being pulled up from street level to the Institute roof along with their feeding table. But that was apparently not high enough. When we continued our experiments in Munich we chose the tallest bombed houses we could find. Later we thought that the vertical rock faces of the Schafberg massiv at Lake Wolfgang were both more suitable and more pleasant experimental sites. On one occasion the hive would be placed at the bottom of a precipice and the feeding table nearly 200 ft higher up on a narrow ridge, another time the observation hive was placed on top and the feeding place below. To reach one from the other on foot you usually had to know your way about mountains pretty well and to take a long walk round— it was zoology at its healthiest and best.

But, although the conditions seemed favourable, somehow the bees always managed to evade a clear answer in the most exasperating fashion. By some means or other they would find a way out of the unusual situation we had put them in and would send their fellow foragers to the desired goal without the need of saying "up" or "down". In the end the Bavarian police helped us to solve this puzzling question by enabling us to work undisturbed on Eschels-bacher Bridge, a structure otherwise much visited by tourists, which spans the river Ammer in a sweeping arch, rising to 250 ft above the river. They also allowed us to work on one of their wireless transmission towers, and there at last the bees, deprived of a rock face that could be used for orientation, were really at their wits' end. Their frantic round dances sent their fellow workers to the meadows around the hive while they themselves spiralled towards the sky. Even the most perfect insects with sheer incredible instincts are not equipped to cope with *unnatural* situations. Normally they will find their way to the blossoms near the top of a tree easily enough without the need for any special direction upwards once they have found the tree itself, and there is never any pie in the sky for them.

Another series of experiments which I carried out with my pupil M. Lindauer was equally enjoyable as out-door exercise and just as exciting. We wanted to find out which was more important for the bees' orientation, terrestrial landmarks or the celestial compass (cf. p. 156). We tried to make these two modes of orientation contradict each other. One day, for instance, we would make the bees fly from the hive to the feeding place along the edge of a forest running due north–south, and the next day they would find themselves close to another forest border running due west–east, so that the guiding line of the forest conflicted with the celestial compass. In such a situation they would fly along the edge of the forest and take no notice of the sky. However, when their

FIG. 37. Healthy zoology in the mountains. The hive under observation (not seen in the picture) stands at the foot of an over-hanging rock face 60 ft high. Marked bees gather on a suspended feeding table and are pulled up gradually to the top of the rock face exactly above the entrance to the hive. Will the dances on the combs indicate to the fellow foragers the upward direction? The observer signals by trumpet that the feeding table should be pulled up one step further. See also Fig. 38.

line of flight, though parallel to the edge of the forest, was some distance away from it, their behaviour changed. Once a certain distance had been exceeded, i.e. once the landmark ceased to be conspicuous, the celestial compass took over. In this way, using all kinds of landmarks, we were able to elucidate the relative importance of different aids to orientation. Experiments of this nature took us on longish trips into the Bavarian countryside. Yet others involved long journeys into distant lands. In that case, however, I left the actual job of travelling to the younger men.

There are only four species of social honey-bees (*Apis*) known to zoologists; of these, only one, *Apis mellifera*, occurs in

FIG. 38. On top of the rock face. The feeding table has arrived at the top. The pole, in front, with the tin can serves as "airmail line" communication for the observers. The distance between the hive and the feeding place was too great for oral communication.

Europe. The rest are natives of India where, presumably, the genus had its origin. With the help of a grant from the Rockefeller Foundation, Dr. Lindauer went on a study tour to India and Ceylon in order to engage in what we called "comparative philology" of the bees' language. He wanted chiefly to find out whether among the Indian bees there existed some simpler forms of communication which might be regarded as precursors of the highly complex system used by European honey-bees. We hoped that if this were so it might perhaps throw some light on the phylogenetic development of this method of communication. Our hopes were not disappointed. He studied the minute species *Apis florea*, insects only about half the size of ordinary domestic flies but much more colourful and glamorous. They are more primitive than our honey-bees in a number of ways and build a single honey-comb, about the size of a man's palm, on some branch right in the open, without protection of any kind. He found that these bees communicate with each other on the same principle as their European cousins, except that they do not translate the direction in relation to the sun to a direction in relation to the force of gravity (cf. p. 143); they can only indicate direction by immediate reference to the position of the sun, as our bees do when they are made to dance on a horizontal surface. Hence they have to build their nests in the open, and hence they always build a sort of horizontal platform for their dance rituals by enlarging and smoothing the top surface of their single horizontal honeycomb.

Even more primitive means of communication were shown to exist among the unarmed social bees of Ceylon, which are more distant relations of our honey-bees. There are a great many genera of these unarmed bees (*Meliponidae*) of varying degrees of social differentiation so that we may be justified in our hopes that further discoveries regarding their communication behaviour will help our understanding of the origin of the bees' language.

While these researches meant journeys to the east, another investigation involved a journey west across the Atlantic. The history of that particular problem dates back some 30 years. Following a chance observation by A. Forel I had tried to train bees to keep very strictly to settled meal-times and found that this was much easier than I had expected. Somewhat later, Inge Beling, a pupil of mine, did some painstaking work on the bees' time sense for her thesis. Other studies followed. What surprised us most was the fact that bees could be so trained in enclosed places artificially illuminated day and night, and once even deep down in a mine. The most probable assumption was that the bees possessed some-how an "internal clock". But it was also conceivable that they responded to some unknown form of radiation of regular diurnal periodicity which penetrates not only into the interior of buildings but also into the bowels of the earth.

To decide this question I had planned to train a group of bees in Hamburg to feed at a definite hour of German mean time and to find out during a voyage across the Atlantic whether they would keep to that time or adapt to local time as the boat sped westward. Unfortunately my first attempt miscarried because the woman student who was to observe the bees during the crossing was too seasick to do anything. Then came the war, which meant that for a long time there was no chance of repeating the experiment. This may actually have been a good thing. For with the opportunities offered by air travel after the war the original plan of the experiment could be much improved. Friends in Paris and New York helped to make it a success. Because flight connections to New York were most favourable from Paris, Dr. M. Renner, my collaborator in this work, trained his bees in Professor Grassé's Paris laboratory. At the American end, Professor T. Schneirla saw to it that the bees were whisked through the customs immediately on arrival by air and taken straight to a room at the American Museum of Natural History which was the exact counterpart of the room where they had been trained. Twenty-four hours after their last meal in Paris they punctually turned up at their little food dish in New York. This proved without a doubt that they possessed an internal clock.

Not that we had solved thereby the last mystery of their time sense. By no means. Science advances but slowly, with halting steps. But does not therein lie her eternal fascination? And would we not soon tire of her if she were to reveal her ultimate truths too easily?

*　*　*　*　*

While we are children we live entirely in the present. Later we learn to look ahead. And when old age catches up with us we like to look back: back over a long winding road half shrouded in the mists of the past. Here we see it pass through a cold sunless valley where sheer impenetrable thickets threaten to bar the way; there it leads to lofty heights where beautiful vistas reward the pilgrim. And always there are flowers by the wayside, beautiful and strange.

It is easier to dream about these things than to recapture the fleeting, insubstantial shades of the past and make them come to life again on the printed page.

> I have attempted it—Did I succeed?
> But after all—you did not *have* to read!
> And yet you did? That I thus held your mind,
> Touching, perhaps, a cord within your breast,
> Would mean the best reward that I could find,
> The hoped for consummation of my quest.

> Ich hab's versucht
> Und weiß nicht, ob's gelungen.
> Mein Trost: zum Lesen
> Warst Du nicht gezwungen.
> Hast Du's getan
> Und bist nicht abgesprungen?
> Hat eine Saite
> In Dir angeklungen?
> So wäre es
> Für meiner Feder Fleiß
> Der still erhoffte
> Und der schönste Preis.

PUBLISHED WORKS

by Prof. Karl von Frisch

BOOKS

1. *Sechs Vorträge über Bakteriologie für Krankenschwestern,* Vienna and Leipzig 1918.
2. *Aus dem Leben der Bienen. Verständl. Wissenschaft,* vol. 1, Springer-Verlag 1927 (7th ed. 1964).
3. *Du und das Leben. Eine moderne Biologie für Jedermann.* Verlag Ullstein 1936 (last re-edition 1966). English edition: *About Biology,* Oliver & Boyd, Edinburgh and London 1962; American edition, revised: *Man and the Living World,* Harcourt, Brace & World, New York 1963.
4. *10 kleine Hausgenossen.* Heimeran-Verlag, Munich 1940 (5th ed., Kosmos Verlag 1966); *Ten Little Housemates,* English transl. edition, Pergamon Press, Oxford.
5. *Duftgelenkte Bienen im Dienst der Landwirtschaft und Imkerei.* Springer-Verlag, Vienna 1947.
6. *Biologie* (for secondary schools). 2 vols., Bayr. Schulbuchverlag, Munich 1952/53 (3rd ed. in press). English translation: *Biology,* Harper & Row, New York, Evanstone and London 1964.
7. *Bienenfibel.* Bruckmann-Verlag, Munich 1954.
8. *Erinnerungen eines Biologen,* Springer-Verlag, Berlin–Göttingen–Heidelberg 1957. 2nd ed. (unchanged) 1962. The original of this volume.
9. *Sprache und Orientierung der Bienen.* Dr. Albert Wander Memorial Lecture, No. 3, Berne and Stuttgart 1961. 2nd ed. 1964.
10. *Das kleine Insektenbuch.* Insel-Verlag, Leipzig 1961.
11. *Tanzsprache und Orientierung der Bienen,* pp. 578, 432 figs., Springer-Verlag, Berlin–Heidelberg–New York 1965. English translation, Harvard University Press, Cambridge, Mass. (in press).

ARTICLES

1. Studien über die Pigmentverschiebung im Facettenauge. *Biol. Zbl.* **28**, 662–671, 698–704 (1908).
2. Über die Beziehungen der Pigmentzellen in der Fischhaut zum sympathischen Nervensystem. *Festschrift f. Richard Hertwig,* vol. 3, 15–28, Jena 1910.—*Dissertation.*
3. Über das Parietalorgan der Fische als funktionierendes Organ. *Sitzgsber. Ges. f. Morph. u. Physiol.* Munich 1911.

4. Beiträge zur Physiologie der Pigmentzellen in der Fischhaut. *Arch. f. Physiol.* **138**, 319–387 (1911).
5. Über den Einfluß der Temperatur auf die schwarzen Pigmentzellen der Fischhaut. *Biol. Zbl.* **31**, 236–248 (1911).
6. Über den Farbensinn der Fische. *Verh. Dtsch. zool. Ges.* 1911, 220–225.
7. Über farbige Anpassung bei Fischen. *Zool. Jahrb. (Phys.)* **32**, 171–230 (1912) *(Dissertation)*.
8. Über Färbung und Farbensinn der Tiere. *Sitzgsber. Ges. f. Morph. u. Physiol.* Munich 1912.
9. Sind die Fische farbenblind? *Zool. Jahrb. (Phys.)* **33**, 107–126 (1912).
10. Über die Farbanpassung des Crenilabrus. *Zool. Jahrb. (Phys.)* **33**, 151–164 (1912).
11. Über den Farbensinn der Bienen und die Blumenfarben. *Münch. med. Wschr.* 1913, No. 1.
12. (with KUPELWIESER): Über den Einfluß der Lichtfarbe auf die phototaktischen Reaktionen niederer Krebse. *Biol. Zbl.* **33**, 517–552 (1913).
13. Zur Frage nach dem Farbensinn der Tiere. *Verh. Ges. dtsch. Naturforscher u. Ärzte* (1913).
14. Weitere Untersuchungen uber den Farbensinn der Fische. *Zool. Jahrb. (Phys.)* **34**, 43–68 (1913).
15. Demonstration von Versuchen zum Nachweis des Farbensinnes bei angeblich total farbenblinden Tieren. *Verh. dtsch. zool. Ges.* **1914**, 50–58.
16. Der Farbensinn und Formensinn der Biene. *Zool. Jahrb. (Phys.)* **35**, 1–188 (1915).
17. Über den Geruchsinn der Biene und seine Bedeutung für den Blumenbesuch. *Verh. zool.-bot. Ges.* Vienna 1915.
18. Zur Kenntnis sozialer Instinkte bei solitären Bienen. *Biol. Zbl.* **38**, 183–188 (1918).
19. Über den Geruchsinn der Biene und seine Bedeutung für den Blumenbesuch. II. Mitt., *Verh. zool.-bot. Ges.* Vienna 1918.
20. (gemeinsam mit O. v. FRISCH): Über die Behandlung difform verheilter Schußbrüche des Oberschenkels. *Arch. klin. Chir.* **109**, No. 4 (1918).
21. Zur Streitfrage nach dem Farbensinn der Bienen. *Biol. Zbl.* **39**, 122–139 (1919).
22. Zuralten Frage nach dem Sitz des Geruchsinnes bei Insekten. *Verh. zool.-bot. Ges.* Vienna 1919.
23. Über den Geruchsinn der Biene und seine blütenbiologische Bedeutung. *Zool. Jahrb. (Phys.)* **37**, 1–238 (1919).
24. RICHARD HERTWIGS Lehrbuch der Zoologie. *Naturwiss.* 1920.
25. Über den Einfluß der Vodenfarbe auf die Fleckenzeichnung des Feuersalamanders. *Biol. Zbl.* **40**, 390–414 (1920).

26. Über die „Sprache" der Bienen I. *Münch. med. Wschr.* 1920, 566–569.
27. Über die „Sprache" der Bienen II. *Münch. med. Wschr.* 1921, 509–511.
28. Über den Sitz des Geruchsinnes bei Insecten. *Zool. Jahrb. (Phys.)* **38**, 1–68 (1921).
29. Über die „Sprache" der Bienen III. *Münch. med. Wschr.* 1922, 781–782.
30. Methoden sinnesphysiologischer und psychologischer Untersuchungen an Bienen. *Handbuch der biologischen Arbeitsmethoden,* vol. IV, Part D, pp. 121–178, 1922.
31. Über die „Sprache" der Bienen. Eine tierpsychologische Untersuchung. *Zool. Jahrb. (Phys.)* **40**, 1–186 (1923).
32. Das Promlem des tierischen Farbensinnes. *Naturwiss.* **11**, No. 24 (1923).
33. Über die Verdauung bei Hydra. *Verh. zool.-bot. Ges.* **73**, 37–43 Vienna 1923.
34. Ein Zwergwels, der kommt, wenn man ihm pfeift. *Biol. Zbl.* **43**, 439–446 (1923).
35. Versuche und Bemerkungen zu SCHNURMANN's Hypothese von der Farbenanpassung "total farbenblinder" Fische. *Z. Biol.* **80**, 223–230 (1924).
36. Sinnesphysiologie der Wassertiere. *Verh. dtsch. zool. Ges.* **29**, 21–42 (1924).
37. Sinnesphysiologie und „Sprache" der Bienen. *Naturwiss.* **12** (1924).
38. Prof. Dr. FRANZ DOFLEIN: *Ostdtsch. Naturwart,* No. 1 (1925).
39. Farbensinn der Fische und Duplizitätstheorie. *Z. vergl. Physiol.* **2**, 393–452 (1925).
40. Vergleichende Physiologie des Geruchs- und Geschmackssinnes. *Handbuch der normalen und pathologischen Physiologie,* Vol. 11, pp. 203–239 (1925).
41. (with RÖSCH): Neue Versuche über die Bedeutung von Duftorgan und Pollenduft für die Verständigung im Bienenvolk. *Z. vergl. Physiol.* **4**, 1–21 (1926).
42. Versuche über den Geschmacksinn der Bienen. *Naturwiss.* **15**, No. 14 (1927).
43. Ein Vorschlag für die Wanderimker. Bienenzucht u. Bienenforschung in Bayern. Wachholtz-Verlag 1927.
44. Die Sinnesphysiologie der Bienen. *Naturwiss.* **15**, Nos. 48/49 (1927).
45. Versuche über den Geschmacksinn der Bienen II. *Naturwiss.* **16**, No. 18, 307–315 (1928).
46. Presidential address. *Verh. dtsch. zool. Ges.* 32, Ann. Meeting, 1928.
47. Die biologische Bedeutung von Blumenfarbe und Blütenduft. *Natur u. Museum* 537–544 1928.

48. Über die Labyrinth-Funktionen bei Fischen. *Verh. dtsch. zool. Ges.* 104–112 (1929).

49. Versuche über den Geschmacksinn der Bienen III. *Naturwiss.* **18**, 169–174 (1930).

50. The sense of hearing in fishes. *Science* **71**, No. 1846, 515 (1930).

51. Über den Gehörsinn der Tiere. *Natur u. Museum* 245–247 (1931).

52. Über den Sitz des Gehörsinnes bei Fischen. *Verh. dtsch. zool. Ges.* 99–108 (1931).

53. (with STETTER): Untersuchungen über den Sitz des Gehörsinnes bei der Ellritze. *Z. vergl. Physiol.* **17**, 686–801 (1932).

54. Die Erforschung des Gehörsinnes bei Fischen. *Wien. klin. Wschr.* No. 20 (1933).

55. Das neue zoologische Institut in München. *Biologe* **2**, 10 (1933).

56. Einige Versuche und Modelle für den zoologischen Schulunterricht. *Unterrichtsbl. Math. u. Naturwiss.* **40**, No. 1 (1934).

57. Über eine Scheinfunktion des Fischlabyrinthes. *Naturwiss.* **22**, 332–334 (1934).

58. Über den Geschmacksinn der Biene. *Z. vergl. Physiol.* **21**, 1–156 (1934).

59. (with TH. KOLLMANN): Der Neubau des Zoologischen Institutes der Universität München. Verlag Hueber 1935.

60. Riechen und Schmecken bei Menschen und bei Tieren. *Natur u. Volk* **65**, 269–283 (1935).

61. (with DIJKGRAAF): Können Fische die Schallrichtung wahrnehmen? *Z. vergl. Physiol.* **22**, 641–655 (1935).

62. Über den Gehörsinn der Fische. *Biolog. Reviews* **11**, 210–246 (1936).

63. Psychologie der Bienen. *Z. Tierpsychol.* **1**, 9–21 (1937).

64. Der Beobachtungsstock in der Schule. *Biologe* **6**, 171–172 (1937).

65. Vom Sinnesleben und Geistesleben der Bienen. *Dtsch. Imkerführer* **11**, No. 6 (1937).

66. RICHARD VON HERTWIG: Obituary, *Münch. med. Wschr.* 1937, No. 45.

67. The sense of hearing in fish. *Nature* (London) **141**, 8 (1938).

68. RICHARD VON HERTWIG: Commemoration address, Verl. d. Bayr. Akad. d. Wiss. 1938.

69. Über die Bedeutung des Sacculus und der Lagena für den Gehörsinn der Fische. *Z. vergl. Physiol.* **25**, 703–747 (1938).

70. Zur Psychologie des Fisch-Schwarmes. *Naturwiss.* **26**, 601–606 (1938).

71. Die Tänze und das Zeitgedächtnis der Bienen im Widerspruch. *Naturwiss.* **28**, 65–69 (1940).

72. Nervöse und hormonale Regelung des tierischen Farbwechsels. *Sitzgsber. Ges. f. Morph. u. Physiol. München* **49** (1940).

73. Die Bedeutung des Geruchsinnes im Leben der Fische. *Naturwiss.* **29**, 321–333 (1941).

N

74. KARL ESCHERICH zum 70. Geburtstage. *Naturwiss.* **29**, 561–563 (1941).
75. Über einen Schreckstoff der Fischhaut und seine biologische Bedeutung. *Z. vergl. Physiol.* **29**, 46–145 (1941).
76. Die Werbetänze der Bienen und ihre Auslösung. *Naturwiss.* **30**, 269–277 (1942).
77. Der Farbwechsel der Fische. *Umschau* 1942, No. 17.
78. Die Bedeutung von SPRENGELS blütenbiologischer Entdeckung. *Dtsch. Imkerführer* **16**, No. 9 (1942).
79. CHRISTIAN KONRAD SPRENGELS Blumentheorie vor 150 Jahren und heute. *Naturwiss.* **31**, 223–229 (1943).
80. Die Lenkung des Bienenfluges durch Duftstoffe. *Dtsch. Imkerführer* **17**, No. 1 (1943).
81. Bericht über die am Müchner Zool. Institut eingeleiteten Nosemaarbeiten zur Frage der Vorbeugungsmittel, der chemotherapeutischen Bekämpfung und des Beobachtungsdienstes. *Dtsch. Imkerführer* **16**, No. 12 (1943).
82. Versuche über die Lenkung des Bienenfluges durch Duftstoffe. *Naturwiss.* **31**, 454–459 (1943).
83. Kurzer Bericht über die im Jahre 1943 durchgeführten Versuche über die Lenkung des Bienenvolkes durch Duftstoffe. *Dtsch. Imkerführer* **18**, No. 1 (1944).
84. Kurzer Bericht über die im Jahre 1943 durchgeführten Versuche zur Bekampfung der Nosemaseuche der Bienen. *Dtsch. Imkerführer* **18**, No. 2 (1944).
85. Die „Sprache" der Bienen und ihre Nutzanwendung in der Landwirtschaft. *Experientia (Basel)* **2**, No. 10 (1946).
86. Die Tänze der Bienen. *Österr. zool. Z.* **1**, 1–48 (1946).
87. *Medizinstudium und Biologieunterricht.* J. A. Kienreich, Graz 1947.
88. RICHARD HESSE: Obituary *Almanach österr. Akad. Wiss. für 1945*, **95** (1947).
89. Gelöste und ungelöste Rätsel der Bienensprache. *Naturwiss.* **35**, Nos. 1, 2 (1948).
90. Die Polarisation des Himmelslichtes als orientierender Faktor bei den Tänzen der Bienen. *Experientia (Basel)* **5**, 142–148 (1949).
91. Die Sonne als Kompaß im Leben der Bienen. *Experientia (Basel)* **6**, 210–221 1950.
92. Orientierungsvermögen und Sprache der Bienen. *Naturwiss.* **38**, 105–112 (1951).
93. Spitzenleistungen tierischer Sinnesorgane unde ihre biologische Bedeutung. *Vjschr. naturforsch. Ges. Zürich* **96**, 176–178 (1951).
94. Hummeln als unfreiwillige Transportflieger. *Natur u. Volk* **82**, 171–174 (1952).
95. Die wechselseitigen Beziehungen und die Harmonie im Bienenstaat. *Coll. internat. du Centre nat. de la Recherche scient.* **34**, Paris 1952.

96. KARL ESCHERICH: *Jahrb. Bayr. Akad. d. Wiss.* 1952.
97. „Sprache" oder „Kommunikation" der Bienen? *Psychol. Rdsch.* **4**, 235–236 (1953).
98. (with HERAN and LINDAUER): Gibt es in der „Sprache" der Vienen eine Weisung nach oben oder unten? *Z. vergl. Physiol.* **35**, 219–245 (1953).
99. Eine eigenartige Räuberbande. *Z. Bienenforsch.* **2** (1953).
100. Die Richtungsorientierung der Bienen. *Verh. dtsch. zool. Ges. Freiburg 1952,* pp. 58–72, Liepzig 1953.
101. Die Fähigkeit der Bienen, die Sonne durch die Wolken wahrzunehmen. *Sitzgsber. Bayr. Akad. Wiss., Math.-Naturwiss. Kl.* 1953.
102. (with LINDAUER): Himmel und Erde in Konkurrenz bei der Orientierung der Bienen. *Naturwiss.* **41**, 245–253 (1954).
103. Symbolik im Reich der Tiere. *Münchner Universitätsreden,* n.s., No. 7, Verlag Heuber, München 1954.
104. *Sprechende Tänze im Bienenvolk.* Festrede am 11. 12. 54. Verlag der Bayr. Akad d. Wiss. 1955.
105. (with LINDAUER): Über die Fluggeschwindigkeit der Bienen und über ihre Richtungsweisung bei Seitenwind. *Naturwiss.* **42**, 377–385 (1955).
106. Beobachtungen und Versuche M. LINDAUERS an indischen Bienen. *Sitzgsber. Bayr. Akad. Wiss., Math.-Naturwiss. Kl.* 1955.
107. EUGEN KORSCHELT: Obituary. *Almanach österr. Akad. Wiss.* **105** (1956).
108. (with LINDAUER): The "language" and orientation of the honey bee. *Annual Rev. Entomol.* **1**, 45–58 (1956).
109. Die Sinne der Bienen im Dienst ihrer sozialen Gemeinschaft. *Nova Acta Leopoldina* N.F. **17**, No. 122 (1956).
110. Lernvermögen und erbgebundene Tradition im Leben der Bienen. Lecture 18. 6. 1954. L'instinct dans le comportement des animaux et de l'homme. Fondation Singer-Polignac, pp. 345–386. Paris 1956.
111. The "language" and orientation of the bees. *Proc. Amer. Philos. Soc.* **100**, 515–519 (1956).
112. Wie Insekten in die Welt schauen. *Studium gen.* **10**, 204–210 (1957).
113. Über den Schwänzeltanz der Bienen (mit R. JANDER). *Z. vergl. Physiol.* **40**, 239–263 (1957).
114. Neues von der „Sprache" und Orientierung der Bienen, *Vierteljahresschrift du. Naturforsch. Gesellsch. in Zürich,* **102**, Final number 1957.
115. Die Bienen und ihr Himmelskompass, *Orden Pour le Mérite für Wissenschaften u. Künste, Reden und Gedenkworte,* 1956/7, **2**, 135–161, Heidelberg 1958.
116. Die Erforschung der Sinnesleistungen bei Insekten. *Mitt. d. Schweizer. Entomolog. Gesellsch.* **31**, 139–145 (1958).

117. Über Zeichnungsmuster auf Schmetterlingsflügeln. *Sitzungsber. Bayer. Akademie d. Wissensch. Mathem.-Naturwiss. Kl.* 157–165, Munich 1958.

118. HANS WINTERSTEIN zum 80. Geburtstag. *Ärztliche Praxis* **31**, 1052 (1959).

119. Insekten die Herren der Erde. *Naturwissenschaftl. Rundschau,* 369–375 (1959).

120. Bestrafte Gefrässigkeit. *Z. f. Tierpsychologie,* **16**, 647–650 (1959).

121. Über den Farbensinn der Insekten. *Proceedings of the International Symposium* (Paris 1958), 19–28 (1960).

122. Wie erkennt die Biene den Sonnenstand bei geschlossener Wolkendecke? *Naturwissenschaftl. Rundschau,* 169–172 (1960).

123. Wunder der Insektenwelt. *Triangel,* **4**, 206–218 (1960). (Wonders of the Insect World, *Triangle* **4**, 206–218, 1960.)

124. ERNST MATTHES (Obituary): *Verhandl. d. Deutsch. Zoolog. Gesellsch. in München 1959,* 532–534, Liepzig 1960.

125. RUTH BEUTLER (Obituary): *Verhandl. d. Deutsch. Zoolog. Gesellsch. in Bonn 1960,* 544–546, Liepzig 1961.

126. Über die „Missweisung" bei den richtungsweisenden Tänzen der Bienen. *Die Naturwissenschaften,* **48**, 585–594 (1961).

127. Über die durch Licht bedingte „Missweisung" bei den Tänzen im Bienenstock. *Experientia,* **18**, 49 et seq. (1962).

128. OTTO RENNER (Obituary): *Orden Pour le Mérite f. Wissenschaften und Künste, Reden u. Gedenkworte,* **4**, 129–137, Heidelberg 1962.

129. (with KRATKY): Über die Beziehung zwischen Flugweite und Tanztempo bei der Entfernungsmeldung der Bienen. *Die Naturwissenschaften,* **49**, 409–417 (1962).

130. Dialects in the language of the bees. *Scientific American,* **207**, 79–87 (1962).

131. Bienen und Blumen. *Kosmos,* **79**, 279–283 (1963).

132. Die Bienen und das Himmelslicht. *Sitzungsbericht Naturforschend. Gesellsch.* (Bern 1960), 1963.

133. Bienenuhr und Blumenuhr. *Zeitsch. f. Tierpsychologie,* **20**, 441–445 (1963).

134. MAX HARTMANN (Obituary), *Orden Pour le Mérite f. Wissensch. u. Künste, Reden u. Gedenkworte,* **6**, 109–115, 1964.

135. Spitzenleistungen im Sinnesleben der Bienen. *24. Kongress Deutscher Gesellschaft f. Psychologie,* 10–23, Göttingen 1965.

INDEX

Abbazzia 19
Abel, O. 43
Academic training methods 116, 123
Actinia 22, 35
 light sensitivity 22
Adriatic 19, 39, 79
Aeroplane, early demonstration 23
Air raids 135, 136
Air-travel 157, 158, 161, 167, 168, 178
Albert Magnus College 111, 158
Alt-Harlaching, see Harlaching
American Army 138 et seq.
American Civil War 114
American journey
American Museum of Natural History 112, 178
 (1930) 111 et seq.
 (1949) 157 et seq.
American universities
 equipment 115
 libraries 116
 staffing 115, 116
Ammer, river 174
Amputations 63
Anatomy, comparative 32
Animal friendships 172
Animal trainer 107
Ann Arbor 113, 164
Ants, island sites for 119
Apiculture, Inspector of 71
Apiculturists, U.S. 169
Apis florea 177
Apis mellifera 176
Apis species 176
Aquarium, first 16
Anschütz-Kaempfe, H. 127

Arco, Count 68
Army Medical Corps 4
Arthropods 156
Augustiner Bräu 48
"Aus dem Leben der Bienen" 107

Bacteriological laboratory 62
Bacteriology, lectures on 64
Balance, sense of, in fish 82, 83, 85, 104
Balkan War 61
Baltic 79, 80, 96
Baltzer, F. 166
Bamberger, G. 73, 130
Basilar membrane 82, 85
Bats, orientation of 70
Bavarian Academy of Science 102
Becher 76, 77
Beebe, W. 159
Beekeepers' organizations 129, 130
Beekeeping in U.S.A. 169
Bees 48, 55–57, 63, 66, 71 et seq., 94, 95, 105 et seq., 113, 129 et seq., 150 et seq., 173 et seq.
 colour training, see Bees, training to colours
 colour vision, see Bees, senses, vision
 communication 173
  primitive means 177
  see also Bees, dances, languages
 dances 72 set seq., 95, 130, 139 et seq., 150 et seq., 173 et seq.
  disorientation 174
  horizontal 150 et seq.

187

Bees – *cont.*
  dances – *cont.*
    indication of distance and direction 139 et seq., 150, 151
    international validity 142 et seq.
    round dance 72, 140
    tailwagging dance 140–3
  demonstration of colour vision 57
  displacement experiment 153
  division of labour 92
  epidemic 129 et seq.
  eyes 152, 156
  as experimental animals 105
  film on 94, 95
  and flowers (mutual adaptation) 55
  Indian 176, 177
  indication of direction up or down 173, 174
  indicating direction
    by reference to sun 150, 151
    by angle with gravity 143
    see also Bees, dances
  internal clock 156, 177, 178
  language 71 et seq., 94, 140, 151 et seq., 173 et seq., 177 et seq.
    phylogenetic development 176, 177
    see also Bees, dances, communication
  lectures on 94, 95, 113
  long distance experiments 73–5
  marking of 72, 74
  Nosema disease 129 et seq.
  observation hives 73, 138, 150
  odour guidance 130, 131
  orientation 152 et seq., 173 et seq.
    blue sky 152
    landmarks 155, 174
    polarized light 152, 153
    by sun 174
  other social 142

  perception of sweetness, *see* Bees, sense of taste
  as pollinators 55, 105, 130
  scent organ 141, 142
  scent training 63, 66, 71
  senses of 48, 55–7, 63, 66, 105–7, 130, 156
    hearing 105
    smell 63, 66, 105, 130
    taste 105–7
    vision 48, 55–7, 152, 153, 156
      colour vision 48, 56–7
      polarized light 152, 153
      sun through cloud 156
    time sense 177, 178
  training to colour and smell 55 et seq., 71
    see also Bees, odour guidance
  training to time 177
  unarmed 177
Bees House (new Institute) 119, 120
Beetles 33
Beling, Inge 177
Berne 166
Benedictine monks 24
Benedikt, Pater 24
Benndorf, H. 152
Beringer, J. B. H. 26
Berkeley 167
Bethe 71
Beutler, Ruth 71, 91, 92, 130, 136, 146
Billed platypus 159
Billroth, T. 1, 17, 59, 60
Biological Club 54
Biological Institute (Harvard), Cambridge, Mass. 158, 159
Biological Institute of Marine Research, Trieste 38 et seq.
Biological Research Station, Prater, Vienna 40, 43, 45
Biologische Station Lunz 54
Biology, and the study of medicine 148
Bird island 80

Bird migration 96
Birth place 1, 2
Bloomington 113
Blue grotto 43
Blue Ribbon of the Atlantic 112
Blue tit 15
Bombing raids 109, 135, 136, 137
Bora 39
Boscotrecase 30
Boveri
  Marcella 111, 112, 158
  Marg. 111
  Th. 34, 47, 103, 111
Bowling alley 14, 23
Brahms 17
Bremen, steamer 112, 157
Breslau 90 et seq., 108
Brioni 39
Brücke 59
Brunnwinkl 3, 13–16, 25 et seq.,
  73, 74, 82, 92, 105, 107,
  120–5, 133–45, 147, 148, 153,
  154
  evacuation to 135 et sq.
  history 28
  museum 25 et seq., 135
  post-war work 138–45
Buchner 47, 52, 56
Buffalo 113
Bullet fractures 63
Bumble bees 131
Busch, Wilh. 58
Busi 43

California 158, 167, 168
California Institute of Technology
  168
Californian Redwood 167
Cambridge, England 153
Cambridge, Mass. 142
Capri 43, 50, 51
Castle Lautrach 127
Cat-fish 83 et seq.
  foodtraining 84
  response to whistling 84

Cave Salamander 119, 126
Celestial compass 155 et seq., 174,
  175
Central State Board for Teaching
  Films 95
Ceylon 176, 177
Chemistry, Department of (Munich)
  147
Chicago 113, 164, 165, 168
  stock yards 113
Chimpanzees 161, 162
Cholera 62
Christmas gifts 2, 8–10
Circus animals, training of 108
Cirsium oleraceum 131
Cleveland, Ohio 113
Clover
  Red 130, 131
  White 131
Cochlea 82, 85
Colloquium (examination for
  Privatdozent) 52
Colour-blindness in fish and inver-
  tebrates
  dispute over 48, 49
  theory of 48
Colour changes 40–43, 49, 52, 71,
  123
  see also Fish, minnows
Colour vision
  demonstration of 57
  in bees 55 et seq.
  in fish 48
  see also Bees, Fishes
  in fishes, and the duplicity theory
    of vision, lecture 113
Colour solutions, toxic 49
Columbia University 113
Columbus, Christopher 79
Columbus, Ohio 113, 164
Communists 69
Comparative Physiology, Handbook
  of 71
Comparative Physiology, see Physiology, comparative
Comparative Physiology, Journal of
  94

Compound eyes, *see* Eyes, Bees, Beetles, Crustaceans, Insects, Lepidoptera
Congo, Belgian   165
Conservator   117
Convergence   86
Cooper, C. Fennimore   114
Cori   38
Cornell University   113, 157, 169
Cowhorn   74
Cows, habit training   165
Cruelty to animals   108, 127
Crustaceans   32, 33, 71, 156, 162
Cyprinids, hearing in   86

Dachauer Moos   37
Dalmatia   38, 42, 43
Dances, *see* Bees, dances
"Dancing bees, the"   107, footnote
Danube valley   40
Darwin   42
Deep sea research   159
Denker, A.   120, 212
Depressive doubts   58, 59
Deutsche Forschungsgemeinschaft   170
Dictatorship of the proletariat in Bavaria   68
Diencephalon   44
Digestion, physiology of   71
Dijkgraaf, S.   104
Distance, indication of, *see* Bees, dances
Diving bell   159
Doctoral examination   42
Doctoral theses
  choosing subjects for   58
  students writing   91
Doctoral thesis, author's   40 et seq., 52
Doflein, F.   37, 38, 54, 91
Dohrn, A.   50
Dohrn, R.   49, 50
Dolomites   37
Dolphins   39, 163, 164

Dorothee, nurse, *see* Frisch, Margarethe von
Driving test   121
Drosophila   168
Duino   39
Duplicity theory of vision   92 et seq.
  lecture   113
Dusensy, Charlotte   5
  Jewish extraction   5, 132
Dysentery   63

Ear
  fish   82 et seq., 83, 86
  human   84, 86
  parrot   120
Earthworms   127
Earrings, Keller's grandmother's   9 et seq.
East Prussia   130
Ebner   32
Ebner-Eschenbach   17
Ehrenberg   50
Einstein   160
Eiselsberg   27
Eisner, Kurt   68
Electric fishing   165
Elephants   108, 160
Elze, C.   81, 164
Emerson   165
Entrance examination   23
Epidemic, bees   129 et seq.
Epp, von   69
Eschelsbacher Bridge   174
Eschelsbacher Brücke   174
Evacuation from Munich   135
Evolution, theory of   42
Examination
  Doctor   42
  entrance   27
  first medical   33
  matriculation   29
  philosophy   42
  Privatdozent   52
Excursions, students'   37, 135

Exner
　　Adolf 5, 7, 16, 29
　　Franz 4, 5
　　Franz Serafin 5, 26, 29, 56, 59, 160
　　Hilde 29
　　Karl 5
　　Marie, *see* Frisch, Marie von
　　Nora 29
　　Sigmund 5, 21, 32, 42, 43, 47, 56, 59, 70, 71, 105
　　brothers 6
　　physiology of the compared eyes of Crustaceans and Insects 32, 70
Eye, frontal of minnows and lizards 43, 44, 104
Eyes
　　bees 152
　　beetles 33
　　crustaceans 32, 33, 71
　　fish 94 et seq.
　　insects 32, 33, 71, 156
　　lepidoptera 33
　　minnows 94 et seq.
　　　frontal 43, 44, 104
　　pigment 33
　　shrimps 33

Falkenberg 77
Fellner, Pater 24
Fertilization
　　day 45
　　of sea urchins' eggs 46
　　see also Pollination
Festival Play (Goldschmidt) 45
Fiddler crabs 162
Field telephones 75
Film, of dancing bees 94, 95
Films, in biological teaching 95, 96
Fire flies 166
Fish
　　colour adaptation 40, 49, 52
　　　blindness, theory of 48, 55
　　　changes 41, 42, 123

collection 26
ear of 82, 83, 86
exotic 19
eye of 92–94
　　frontal eye, *see* Minnows
food training 44, 48, 84, 93, 104
formation of pigment 40
labyrinth 83, 85–87
lateral line system 104
luminous organs 159
neurosecretery cells 44
operations on 85 et seq., 104
organs of equilibrium 82, 85
retina 92, 93
sense of equilibrium 85, 104
sense of hearing 82 et seq., 104, 123, 126
　　difference among species 85–87
　　distinction of pitch 85
　　lecture on 113
　　localizing sound 123
sense of smell 125
sense of taste 104
sense of vision 48, 49, 93, 113, 126
　　colour vision 48, 49, 126
　　in bright and dim light 93
　　lecture on 113
swim-bladder 86
symbol of Christ 108, footnote
tactile sense 85, 126
warning substance 124 et seq.
Weberian ossicles 86
Fishing, electrical 165
Fleas, dying out of 121
Florida 161 et seq.
Flowers
　　colours 53
　　nectar 55, 105
　　pollination 53
Food-training, *see* Bees, Fish
Football 48
Forebears 3
Forel, A. 178
Fossils 26, 27

Franz Ferdinand, Archduke 60
Freiburg 57, 98, 152
Frisch
 Anton von senior 3
 Anton von Professor 1, 2, 3, 11, 12, 13, 16, 19, 44, 53, 59, 66
 Ernst von 18, 27
 Hans von 18, 21, 27, 28, 74
 Helene von 90, 91
  married, Pflünger 133, 148, 171
 Jenny von 65
 Johanna von 67, 73, 88, 90
  married Schreiner 134, 138, 171
 Karl von, photographs 1, facing p. 18, 28, 41, 92, 122, 171, 173
 Margarethe von, née Mohr 64–67, 68, 70, 73, 79, 80, 81, 88, 89, 121, 133, 136, 147, 157, 161, 162, 171, 173
 Maria von 69, 90, 136, 171
 Marie von, née Exner 2, 3, 5, 7, 8–11, 12, 14, 17, 18, 19, 21, 39, 58, 59, 67, 69, 90, 98, 99–101, 136, 171
  letters 8–11, 14, 58, 59, 99
  portraits 7, 12, 100
 Otto von jr. 112, 122, 134, 148, 171, 172
 Otto von sen. 18, 27–29, 61 et seq.
Frauenkirche, Munich 72 (Fig. 17), 167
Frogs 19
Frontal eye
 of lizards 43
 of minnows 43, 44, 104
Frontier, Austrian/German 127, 139, 148

Geffken 77
Geinitz 77
German Science 116, 123

German Society for Natural Science and Medicine, Innsbruck Meeting 94, 96
German Zoological Society Meetings
 Freiburg 57
 Königsberg 96
 Munich 102
Glowworms 166
Goldschmidt, R. 37, 45, 48, 53, 56, 57, 107, 126, 127, 167
Grado 39
Grand Canyon 168
Grandchildren 138, 171 (Fig. 35)
Grandmother, ancestry of 131
Grassé 178
Grasshoppers, protective colouring 162
Graz 146 et seq., 160, 169, 173
Griffin, D. R. 157, 158, 169
Grobben, K. 31, 34, 42
Gulls 80
Gyroscopic compass 127

Habit training
 cows 165
 parakeet 22
Hamburg 178
Harlaching 108
 bombing 136
 rebuilding 170, 171
Harrison, A. G. 112, 115, 158
Harvard University 113, 159
 laboratories 113
Hasler, A. D. 138, 139, 165, 166
Hatschek, B. 34
Hauser, Ilse 34
Haydn quartets 29
Hayes 161
Hearing
 in bees, see Bees, sense of hearing
 in fishes, see Fishes, sense of hearing
 in minnows, see Minnows, sense of hearing
Heather 131

Heider, K.   45
Helmholtz   82
Heran   173
Hertwig, O. von   35
Hertwig, R. von   34 et seq., 40,
    42, 45, 49, 53, 56, 57, 60, 76,
    97, 103, 117
  as administrator   47
  appointment to Munich chair
    103
  book on Actinia   35
  co-founder of experimental
    zoology   36
  essays in honour of   47
  fertilization day   46
  festivities, birthday   45
  offering me assistantship   45
  retirement   98
  seminar   38
  textbook of zoology   36
Hess, C. von   48, 49, 57, 84
Heydweiler, A.   76, 78
Himmer, A.   71
Hinterbrühl   66
Hofmann   72
Holtfreter, J.   117, 147
Honey-bees, see Bees
Honeymoon   66
Honey yields, American   169
Hormones in lepidoptera   158
Humanist Gymnasium   18
Humming birds   159
Hungary   1, 19
Hydrobiological research station
    54

Ignaz   21
Inaugural lecture, Graz   148
India   142, 176
Indian mounds   114
Indians, red   114
Indication of direction, see Bees,
    dances
Inflation   88, 89
Innsbruck   45, 94

Insects (other than bees)   25, 26,
    33, 63, 64, 70, 156, 158, 162
Institute of Hygiene   62
Internal Clock   156, 177, 178
International Education Board
    109, 111
Illyria   43
Iron Cross (decoration)   4
Ischl   138
Istria   19, 38
Ithaca   114, 157, 158, 169

Jacksonville Airport   161
Jacobs, W.   147
Jennings   38
Jungle laboratory, Trinidad   159

Kaiser Wilhelm Gesellschaft   54
Kaiser Wilhelm Inst. Biol.   111,
    120
Karplus   33
Kauffungen   64
Keller, Gottfried   7 et seq., 99
  Das Verlorene Lachen   11
  death   17
  letters   8 et seq., 99
  watercolour   9
  visit to See am Mondsee   7
  to Vienna   11
  wedding poem   12
Kerner, v. Marilaun   31
Kiepenheuer, O.   152
Kinsey, A. C.   113
Koehler, O.   48, 51
Kollmann, Th.   117
Königsberg   96, 97
Körner, O.   83, 84
Kotor   43
Kreidl   71
Kranz   97
Krogh, A.   152
Kupelwieser, C.   54
Kupelwieser, H.   54
Kurische Nehrung   96

Labiau 96
Laboratory, bacteriological 62
Laboratory for Primate Behaviour 161, 162
Ladenburg, J. von 5
Labyrinth (of fishes and other vertebrates) 81, 82, 83
Lake District, Austrian 7
   see also Brunnwinkl, Lake Wolf-gang, St Gilgen, Mondsee, and Schafberg
Lake Wolfgang 3, 13 et seq., 20, 25, 123–5, 134–6, 174
Landmarks see Bees, orientation
Lang 59
Langenwerder 80
Language of the bees, the, lecture 113
   see also Bees, language
Lashley, K. S. 161
Lateral line system 104
Lautrach 127
Lecture(s)
   author's
      bacteriology 64
      bees 57, 94, 113, 157 et seq.
      comparative physiology 70
      first 25, 52, 53
      fish 25, 113
      inaugural, Graz 148
      test 52, 53
      tours 111 et seq., 147 et seq.
   Exner's on human physiology 34
   Hertwig's on comparative an-atomy 36
Lecture hall
   Graz 149
   Munich 110, 120
Lepidoptera
   compound eyes 33
   hormones 158
   pupal development 158
Lice 63, 64
Liebig 103
Light sensitivity
   of blind fish 43, 44, 104
   of sea anemones 22
Lindauer, M. 142, 173
Lithographia Wirceburgensis 26
Löhr 24
London 169
Los Angeles 168
Lovrana 19, 38
Löwenstein 104
Ludwig 1st, King of Bavaria 102
Lunz 54

Macropods 67
Madison 113, 114, 165, 166
Major Zoological Practical 37, 40, 47, 116
Mantis religiosa 40
Marées, H. V. 50
Marien-Klause (St Mary's Close) 109
Marine fauna 19, 39, 50, 79, 159
Marine Land 163
Marine research stations
   Naples 49 et seq.
   Pacific Grove 168
   Trieste 38 et seq.
Max Planck Gesellschaft 54, 111, 120
May, Karl 114
Mecklenburg 78
   patois 79
Medical curriculum 148, 149
Medicine
   practising of 63 et seq.
   study of 31 et seq.
Meliponidae 177
Mendota, Lake 166
Meyer, H. H. 34, 101
Michigan, Lake 165
Ministry of Education
   Austrian 148
   Bavarian 132
   Schwerin 76
   see also Reichsminister of Educa-tion
Ministry of Food 129, 133
Minneapolis 166

Minnich, D. E.   113, 166
Minnows   40, 41, 43, 44–8, 83–7,
    93, 104, 105, 113, 123–6
  as experimental animals   104,
    105, 126
  colour adaptation   40
  colour changes   41, 43
  ear   83, 86, 104
  eye, frontal   43, 104
  food training   44, 48, 84
  labyrinth   83
  lateral line system   104
  sense of equilibrium   104
  sense of hearing   84 et seq., 104,
    123, 126
    acuity   84
    location of sound   123
    pitch   85
  sense of smell   125, 126
  sense of taste   104, 126
  tactile sense   85, 126
  warning substance   124, 125
  Weberian ossicles   86
Misenum, Cape   50
Mohr, Margarethe, see Frisch, Mar-
    garethe von, née Mohr
Mondsee, Lake   7, 9, 16
  watercolour   10
Monterey   168
Morgan, Th. H.   168
Mormyrids   74, 87
Mostar   43
Motor car   121
Müller, L.   42
Müllerlieder   14
München, Steamer   112
Munich   22, 34–40, 45–59, 68–75,
    98–145, 146, 148, 149, 170–6
  Assistant at   45–51
  Assistant Professor at   68–75
  Augustiner-Bräu   48
  bombardment of   135, 136, 137
  lecturer at   52–59
  Meeting of German Zoological
    Society   102, 103
  New Institute   117–30
  Oktoberwiese   171

post-war conditions
  1st World War   68, 69
  2nd World War   146
Professor at   98–145, 170 et seq.
student at   34–40
University of, see Munich, and
    Zoological Institute, Munich
Müritz   80
Music   27, 28, 68, 81, 82

Naples   30, 49, 50, 52
  Museum   50
  Zoological Station   49 et seq.
National Academy of Sciences,
    Washington   114
National selection, theory of   42
National Socialism   70, 78, 95,
    109, 117, 126–9, 131–5
Neu-Harlaching, see Harlaching
Neurospora   168
New Haven (Yale)   112, 142, 158
New Institute (of Zoology, Munich)
    117–20
  animal quarters   119–20
  lecture hall   120
  staff room   118
New York   112 et seq., 157, 159,
    160, 168, 169, 178
  harbour   112
  La Guardia Airport   157
  Museum of Natural History
    159, 160, 178
  skyline   112
  Zoological Gardens   159
Newts   19
Niagara Falls   113
"Nobility"   3
Nosema apis   129
Nosema Council   129
Nurse Dorothee, see Frisch, Mar-
    garethe von, née Mohr
Nurses' training school   61, 64

Observation hives   73
Oceanarium   163, 164

Odour guidance 130 et seq.
"Old Academy" 35, 102, 104, 117, 118
Old Mill, Brunninkl 3, 13, 14, 16
Oldenbourg, H. 70
Oldenbourg, P. 69
Onondaga Indians 114
Operations on animals 33, 85 et seq., 104
Operations, surgical 63
Orange Park 161
Organs of equilibrium
 crustaceans 71
 fish 82
 terrestrial vertebrates 82
Orientation, see Bats, Bees
Ornithological Station Rossitten 96
Osborn, F. 159
Ossicles
 of the middle ear 86 et seq.
 Weberian 86 et seq.
Otolaryngologists, Society of 120
Owl 172

Pacific Grove 160
Parakeets 21, 22, 172, 173
Parental home 1, 11, 66
Paris 178
Parker, G. H. 113, 158
Parrot
 Australian 172, 173
 Brazilian 21, 22
Parrots, ears of 120
Parthenogenesis 103
Pavlova 5
Perch 125
Pets
 author's 19–22, 67, 172, 173
 Mrs. von Frisch's 15, 16
 Otto's 172
Pfaundler, M. von 112
Pflüger, Ekkeh 133
Pflüger, Helen, see Frisch, Helene von, married Pflüger

Pflüger, Herm 81, 133
Philadelphia 113
Physiology
 comparative 41, 70 et seq.
 manual of 71
 journal of 94
 human 70, 71
 lecture 32
 Professor of, see Exner, Sigmund
Phytothron 168
Piarist Fathers 18
Pigment
 formation in fish 40
 shifts in
  compound eyes 32–3
  fish 40
Pineal body 44
"Plunder Franzl" 138
Polarized light 152, 153, 156
Polaroid 152
Pollination
 of crop plants 129 et seq.
 of flowers 55, 105
 of Red Clover 130
Pompeii 50
Popular writing 107
Portheim, von 43
Pouchet 41
Prague 4, 5
Prater 43
Praying mantis 40
Primates 161, 162
Princeton 113, 158, 160, 166
Privatdozent, appointment as 52 et seq.
Privatdozenten (head of sections) 118
Professorial posts
 Germany 117, 118
 U.S.A. 115
Professorship appointments
 Breslau 90
 Graz 146
 Munich 98, 170
 Rostock 76
Professorship declined, Vienna 101
Prohibition 115

Protective colouring, grasshoppers 162

Proteus anguineus 119

Przibram, H. 40, 41

Quartet playing 27, 28, 81
Queen breeding cage 72
Quidde, L. 68
Quidde, Mrs. 69

Radiolaria 103
Rain of ashes 30
Rape (plant) 131
Ration cards 128
Red Cross 62
Red indians 114, 115
Reichsminister for Education, Science and Learning 131, 132
Religious beliefs 24, 25
Renner, M. 178
Resonance, theory of 82
Retina, physiology of 92, 93
Retirement
  author's threatened 128, 131 et seq.
  Hertwig 97
Retiring age 98
Reuter, Fritz 79
Rhineland 130
Richter, Mrs. 59
Rockefeller, J. D. 109
Rockefeller Foundation 109, 110, 113, 117, 149, 160, 170, 176
  building grants
    Graz 149
    Munich 109, 110, 113
  research grants 149, 170, 176
  travel grants 109
Rocky Mountains 167, 168
Roe deer 172
Roman Catholic Church 24, 25
Rösch, C. A. 91, 92
Rossitten 96, 97
Rostock 76 et seq., 108
  staff 92
Rostock Heath 79

Rothpletz 52
Rotolactor 166
Round dance, *see* Bees, dances
Rudolfinerhaus 60 et seq.
Russia, bees' trials in 130
Rust 132

St. Gilgen 3, 17, 134, 138
  occupation 138
  wedding 134
Salzburg 27, 138
Salzkammergut 7, 13
  railway 13, 16
  see also Lake Wolfgang, Brunnwinkl, St. Gilgen, Schafberg
San Francisco 151, 166, 167
Sarrasani, Circus 107, 108
Scent gland 142
Scent trail 142
Sawmill, Brunnwinkl 14–16
Schafberg 25, 134, 135, 174
Scharrer, E. 44, 104
Schneiderhan, W. 29
Schneirla, C. T. 178
School years 18 et seq.
Schreiner, Peter 138
Schreiner, Th. 134
Schwabing 34, 68, 70, 73, 108
Schubert, F., footnote to p. 14
Schubert, von 102
"Science you can understand" 107
Scistetica marmorata 162
Sea anemones 22
Sea lions 167, 168
Seals 168
Sea urchins 46
Seeing in dim light 92, 93
Seiler, J. 117
Sense of equilibrium
  minnows 104
Sense of hearing
  bees 105
  fishes 82 et seq., 104
    (lecture) 113
  minnows 123, 126

Sense of smell
  bees   63, 66, 79
  minnows   125
Sense of taste
  bees   106, 107
  fish   104
  minnows   126
Sense of touch, fish   104
Senses, physiology of, *see also* Bees,
    Fish and Minnows
Sequoia gigantea   167
Sequoia sempervirens   167
Seyffertitz, Th. von   133
Silurids   86
Sharks   163
  fossil   52
Shrimps   33
Siebold, V.   103
Slugs   78
Social bees, of India   142
Solitary bees   38
Sommerfeld, A.   104
Sonata playing   68
Soviet Republic (of Bavaria)   68
Spallancani, L.   70
Spanish moss   162
Spartakists   69
Specialization, dangers of   116
Spemann, H.   76, 77, 90, 98, 132
Spiders   156
Spiritual difficulties   24
Springer, Ferd.   94
Squalius cephalus   125
Starfish   38
Stazione Zoologica, Naples   49,
    50, 51
Stetter, H.   84, 104
Straubing   136
String quartet   27, 28, 81
Sugars   105, 106.
Swimbladder   86
Switzerland   145

Tailwagging dance, *see* Bees, dances
Teneriffe   103

Termites   164, 165
Test lecture   52, 53
Thienemann, J.   96
Thimig   66
Third Reich, *see* National Socialism
Thorpe, W. H.   153
Tillandsia usneoides   162
Training
  of students   116, 123
  to colours, 48, 55, 57, 93
  to scents   63, 66, 71, 130, 131
  to sounds   85–87, 104
  to time   178
Trau (Trogir)   43
Trinidad   159
Trowbridge, S.   109, 110, 113
Trudel, P. S.   104, 113
Tschocki   22, 23, 172, 173
Tulln airport   157
Turnips   131
Turtles   163
Typhoid   63
Typhus   63

Union Yacht Club   27
U.S.A.   111 et seq., 157 et seq.,
    178
Universities in U.S.A.   115 et seq.
  libraries   116
  staffing   115
University holidays, value of   121,
    122
University of beginners   78
Univerity of Breslau   91, 92
University of California   167
University of Graz   146 et seq.
University of Iowa   113
University of Munich
  history   102, 103
  see also Munich, and Zoological
      Institute, Munich
University of Rostock   76 et seq.
University of Vienna study tours
    42
  see also Vienna

University of Wisconsin 113, 115, 138, 165
University terms 34
Utah 167

Vermin 61, 64
Vertebrates
ears of 82
head segments 53
retina of 92
Vesuvius, Mount 30, 50, 51
Vicky 161
Vienna 1–3, 5, 7, 8, 10, 11, 18–25, 31–33, 39, 44, 53, 59, 60–67, 81, 101, 157
airport 157
birthplace 1
Biological Research Station 40 et seq.
Medical School 1
parental home 1, 2, 6, 62
Prater 43
Professorship declined 101, 102
Rudolfinerhaus 27, 60–67
school years 18 et seq.
University 31 et seq., 101, 102
Vivarium 40
visit by Keller 11
Wurstel prater 40
Zoological Institute 101, 102
Violin playing 28, 68, 81
Vivarium 40

Wachau region 40
War loan 67
Warnemünde 79
Warning substance 124 et seq.
Warnow 79
War time surgery 60 et seq.
Washington 114, 116, 160
Water divining 119, 120
Weaver, W. 160
Weberian ossicles 86
Weddings
Frisch – Exner 12
Frisch – Mohr 66

Pflüger – Frisch 133
Schreiner – Frisch 134
Weiss, P. 164
Weissenbach am Attersee 136
Went, F. H. 168
Wettstein, Fr. von 120
Wettstein, R. 31, 43
Whaling 39
White fish 125
Wieland, H. 147
Wildalpen 66
Wilhelminum 102
Williams, C. 158
Willstätter, R. 106
Winkler, J. 28, 29
Winterstein, H. 71, 81
Wireless transmission tower 174
Witschi, E. 113, 166
Wolfgang, Lake, see Lake Wolfgang
Woodpecker 20, 21
World War I 54, 60–67, 128, 149
World War II 128–39
Wunder, W. 92
Wurstelprater, Vienna 40

Xaverl 84
X-ray photographs 62

Yale 112, 143, 158, 161, 162
Yerkes, R. M. 161, 162
York, steamer 112

Zeitschrift für vergleichende Physiologie 94
Zoological Collection, Munich 102, 109
Zoological Gardens, New York 143
Zoological Institute, Breslau 91 et seq.
Zoological Institute, Graz 146, 149

Zoological Institute, Innsbruck   45
Zoological Institute, Munich
   assistant at   45–49, 52–60, 67,
      70
   assistant Professor at   70 et seq.
   bees experiments at   72, 73
   biological club   54
   bombing of   137, 139
   evacuation to Brunnwinkl   135
   fish experiments   104
   garden courtyard   72
   history of   102, 103
   lectureship   52–60, 67–70
   New Institute   117 et seq.
      animal quarters   118
      architect   117
      lecture hall   120
      staff room   118
   political interference at   127
   postwar conditions   139, 146
      rehabilitation   147, 170
   Professor at   98–146, 170 et seq.
   rebuilding   109, 110, 113
   retirement, threatened   131–3
   staff   37, 47, 54, 103, 104
   staff outings   103, 104
   staff party   104
   study at   34 et seq.
   war work on *Nosema* and odour
      guidance   128–31
   see also Munich, Old Academy,
      and Wilhelminum
Zoological Institute, American   115
Zoological Institute, Rostock   76 et
   seq.
Zoological Institute, Vienna   101
Zoological Museum, Munich   37,
   102
Zoological Practical
   lesser   36
   major   47 et seq., 116
Zoological Research Station, Naples
   49–51
Zoological Society, *see* German
   Zoological Society
Zoology
   experimental   36
   study of   31 et seq.
Zuckerkandl   32, 101
Zurich   7, 8, 143